A Primer of
Human
Neuroanatomy

CYNTHIA REID
M.B., Ch.B.

Second edition

LLOYD-LUKE

A PRIMER OF
HUMAN NEUROANATOMY

A Primer of Human Neuroanatomy

Cynthia Reid
M.B., Ch.B.

Department of Anatomy and Experimental Pathology
University of St. Andrews

Second Edition

LLOYD-LUKE (MEDICAL BOOKS) LTD
49 NEWMAN STREET
LONDON
1983

FIRST EDITION.................. 1978
SECOND EDITION 1983

PRINTED AND BOUND IN ENGLAND BY
HAZELL WATSON AND VINEY LTD
AYLESBURY, BUCKS
ISBN 0 85324 192 9

PREFACE TO SECOND EDITION

The purpose of this book is to provide a foundation on which a student may build an understanding of the human nervous system. It is not the 'last word' on neuroanatomy. One of the aims has been to keep the text short so as to be readable in the limited time available to students.

I am grateful for all the helpful suggestions concerning the first edition which were made by the reviewers and in particular for the enormous interest shown by Professor J. Joseph and Professor R. E. M. Bowden. I thank the many students who have taken the trouble to make useful comments.

In the preparation of this edition I have again had the advantage of the knowledge and good humour of Dr. E. W. T. Morris, the technical expertise of Mr. S. H. Fairhurst and the unfailing assistance of the publishers.

August, 1982

C.R.

PREFACE TO FIRST EDITION

The purpose of this book is to try to fill a need which I have become aware of in the past five years. Students in their study of the human nervous system have great difficulties particularly if the consideration of the nervous system is separated in time from the study of the anatomy of the head and neck.

The plan of the book is to cover the main points in such a way that the practical dissection of the brain is not held up by a lack of basic knowledge of the anatomy. Function is related to structure where possible but the information given is not meant to be the 'last word' on neuroanatomy but a reasonably understandable guide so that a student can progress onto more advanced texts with confidence.

I make no apology for repeating myself, even when such repetition may seem superfluous; some facts cannot be repeated often enough where the nervous system is concerned.

The author expresses her thanks for the kindly advice, contructive criticism and patience of Dr. E. W. T. Morris who read through the manuscript with such diligence. Mr. S. H. Fairhurst's technical assistance was much appreciated and the publishers were always most helpful during the preparation of this book.

June, 1977   C.R.

CONTENTS

CHAPTER I

INTRODUCTION AND DEVELOPMENT

The Divisions of the Nervous System

The nervous system is divided into peripheral and central parts. The peripheral nervous system consists of 31 pairs of spinal nerves, 12 pairs of cranial nerves, ganglia and nerve plexuses.

The central nervous system is divided into the brain and the spinal cord. The brain is subdivided into the cerebral hemispheres and the part of the brain which lies between them, the cerebellum and the brain stem. The brain stem can be further subdivided into the midbrain, pons and medulla oblongata. The medulla oblongata is continuous caudally with the spinal cord.

An alternative description is on a more developmental basis and is as follows:

Forebrain	The two cerebral hemispheres together with the part of the brain which lies between them
Midbrain	Midbrain as above
Hindbrain	Cerebellum, Pons and Medulla oblongata.

The autonomic nervous system is that part of the nervous system which is concerned with the unconscious activities of the viscera, involuntary muscle and glands. It lies partly within the central nervous system and partly outside the central nervous system.

The Cells of the Nervous System

The cells which make up the nervous system are of two types:

1. Nerve cells or neurons;
2. Neuroglial cells.

In addition, there are to be found the usual cells forming the walls of blood vessels.

Nerve cells are specialised for excitation and nerve impulse conduction and are therefore responsible for most of the functional characteristics of nervous tissue. The number of neurons in the human central nervous system has been estimated to be of the order of 14 thousand million.

Figure 1 shows a nerve cell represented diagrammatically. The part of the cell which includes the nucleus is called the cell body. Dendrites are short, branching processes which form a major part of the receptor area of the cell. Most neurons in the central nervous system have

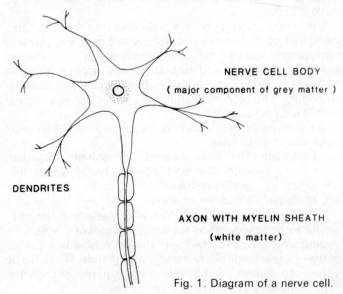

NERVE CELL BODY
(major component of grey matter)

DENDRITES

AXON WITH MYELIN SHEATH
(white matter)

Fig. 1. Diagram of a nerve cell.

several dendrites and are therefore multipolar in shape. Each nerve cell has a single axon which may or may not have a layer of insulating material around it called the myelin sheath.

The nervous system consists of grey and white matter. Grey matter is composed of the cell bodies of neurons surrounded by a network of processes of the neuron itself and terminal fibres arriving from nerve cells elsewhere. White matter is composed of relatively long processes of nerve cells, many of which have myelin sheaths. These long processes are called nerve fibres. Although all nerve cells conform to the general principles already stated there is a wide range of structural variation.

The grey and white matter includes numbers of neuroglial cells which are the interstitial material of the central nervous system. Peripheral nerves have a connective tissue support but this is absent in the central nervous system. The neuroglial cells fall into two categories:

1. The macroglia, comprising the astrocytes and oligodendrocytes which are derived from ectoderm;
2. The microglia, derived from mesoderm, which is assumed to enter the embryonic brain and spinal cord when blood vessels penetrate the developing structures.

Neuroglia, in the broadest sense, should also include the ependymal layer of the central nervous system, the cells which form the myelin of larger nerve fibres (Schwann cells) and the satellite cells found in ganglia (groups of nerve cell bodies lying outside the central nervous system).

The functions of the neuroglial cells are still unconfirmed but it is known that the Schwann cells and the oligodendrocytes participate in the formation of the myelin sheath and that the astrocytes play a role in the repair of injuries. Neuroglial cells may also influence the ionic composition of the extracellular fluid surrounding the nerve cells. Certainly the close relationship of the nerve cells and the neuroglia is evidenced by the fact that neurons do not grow and thrive in tissue culture unless neuro-glial cells are also present.

Some Terms used in Neuroanatomy

An explanation of certain terms used in neuroanatomy must be attempted at this early stage.

A neuron brings its influence to bear on other neurons at junctional points or synapses, a term introduced by ·Sherrington in 1897. There is no joining together of the cytoplasm of the two neurons involved but an interface where they are functionally related. A nerve impulse can be propagated in any direction on the surface of a nerve cell but the direction followed under the physiological conditions is determined by a consistent polarity at the synapse where transmission is from the axon of one neuron to the cell body or processes of another neuron (see Chapter V). Synapses assume a variety of forms, ranging from a simple apposition of axon and dendrite to exceedingly complex arrangements.

The central nervous system is developed from a straight tube which is called the neuraxis. The neuraxis has a head or rostral end and a tail or caudal end. The concept of the neuraxis is useful as, during development, folding occurs which causes changes in position of different components of the central nervous system. It is helpful to retain the idea of the straight tube and, in the anatomical position, to describe ascending fibres as running rostrally and descending fibres as running caudally.

Grey matter (nerve cell bodies and their surrounding processes) and white matter (nerve fibres) are given other names. A collection of grey matter lying outside the central nervous system is called a ganglion. A collection of grey matter lying within the central nervous system is called a nucleus. A group of nerve fibres travelling together from one part of the central nervous system to another part may be called variously a tract, a bundle or a fasciculus. Such a group of nerve fibres will have the same or similar functions.

The Fibres of the Nervous System

Nerve fibres are frequently described with reference to the part of the nervous system with which they are associated. Afferent fibres are transmitting to a structure. The term 'afferent' is used in a general way to describe fibres going towards the central nervous system, such fibres will therefore be transmitting sensory data. Efferent fibres are fibres going away from a structure or away from the central nervous system. They are the axonic processes of nerve cells and carry impulses from the region of the central nervous system in which they arise either to other parts of the central nervous system or to the peripheral nervous system. Efferent fibres will usually be carrying such impulses to striated and non-striated (smooth) muscle and can be described as motor fibres. Striated muscle is subdivided into skeletal muscle and cardiac muscle. Non-striated muscle is involuntary, i.e. not under the direct control of the will. Cardiac muscle, although striated, is involuntary.

Both afferent and efferent nerve fibres are classified on the basis of their function and for this purpose they are divided into seven groups:

1. *General somatic afferent*
   These fibres conduct impulses to the central nervous system from receptors in skin, skeletal muscle and connective tissue;

2. *Special somatic afferent*
   These fibres conduct impulses from receptors in the eyes and the inner ears to the central nervous system; only two cranial nerves are involved;

3. *General visceral afferent*
   These fibres conduct impulses to the central nervous system from receptors in blood vessels, glands, the non-striated (smooth) muscle of the viscera and the striated cardiac muscle;

4. *Special visceral afferent*
   These fibres convey impulses from receptors in the

organs of taste and smell to the central nervous
system;

5. *General somatic efferent*
These fibres conduct impulses from the central
nervous system to the striated muscle of somite
origin;

6. *General visceral efferent*
These fibres conduct impulses from the central
nervous system to the peripheral ganglia of the
autonomic nervous system. (The autonomic nervous
system is that part of the nervous system which is
concerned with the unconscious control of glands,
blood vessels, the non-striated muscle of viscera and
the striated muscle of the heart.);

7. *Special visceral efferent (Branchial motor fibres)*
These fibres convey impulses from the central nervous system to striated muscle which has originated
in the branchial (visceral) arches.

The Autonomic Nervous System

The autonomic nervous system is situated partly inside
and partly outside the central nervous system and it is the
means by which smooth muscle, cardiac muscle, glands
and viscera are controlled. One of the highest levels of the
autonomic nervous system in the central nervous system is
the hypothalamus which is part of the forebrain. Information
is relayed from the hypothalamus to lower centres in the
brain stem and spinal cord. Nerve fibres leave the brain stem
and spinal cord to supply the structures named above.

The autonomic nervous system is divided into two
parts, the sympathetic component and the parasympathetic
component. The general plan is that there is a two-
neuron pathway on the efferent side (see above, Classification of fibres, 6). There is a preganglionic cell in the
central nervous system and its axon synapses in a ganglion
lying outside the central nervous system. In the ganglion
are nerve cell bodies and their fibres leave the ganglion

as postganglionic fibres to supply the viscus, muscle, gland or blood vessel.

The sympathetic and parasympathetic preganglionic neurons are not present throughout the central nervous system. The sympathetic preganglionic neurons are present in the thoracic and upper lumbar regions of the spinal cord, the thoracolumbar outflow. The parasympathetic preganglionic neurons are present in the brain and the sacral region of the spinal cord, the craniosacral outflow. In most cases the sympathetic system has a short preganglionic fibre and a long postganglionic fibre. The parasympathetic system usually has a long preganglionic fibre and a short postganglionic fibre. It follows that the sympathetic ganglia will be near the central nervous system, that is, near the midline, and the parasympathetic ganglia will be near the structure to be supplied. Anatomically this is found to be the case.

Many organs receive an autonomic supply from the parasympathetic and the sympathetic parts of the autonomic nervous system and frequently the two parts of the autonomic nervous system are antagonistic in function.

The Peripheral Nervous System

The peripheral nervous system is composed of 31 pairs of spinal nerves, (Fig. 2) 12 pairs of cranial nerves and the ganglia and plexuses of the autonomic nervous system. The cranial nerves will be considered later; some of the cranial nerves are not truly peripheral.

There are 31 pairs of spinal nerves, arranged in the following way: 8 cervical; 12 thoracic; 5 lumbar; 5 sacral and 1 coccygeal. The first pair of cervical nerves emerges between the skull and the first cervical vertebra. The 8th pair of cervical nerves emerges through the intervertebral foramina between the 7th cervical vertebra and the first thoracic vertebra. The more caudal spinal nerve pairs emerge from the intervertebral foramina bounded

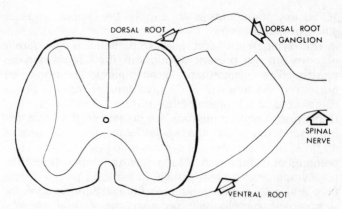

Fig. 2. Typical spinal nerve.

above by the pedicles of the vertebra of the same number.

Each spinal nerve has two roots, a dorsal root (afferent) which has a ganglion on it and a ventral root (efferent). The definitive spinal nerve is therefore a mixture of afferent and efferent fibres.

The purpose of the peripheral nerves is to carry sensory information to the central nervous system and to carry instructions from the central nervous system to the muscles and viscera. The general sensory endings are scattered throughout the body and change physical stimuli into an action potential in nerve endings. There are three classes of sensory endings:

1. Exteroceptors, which respond to stimuli from the external environment resulting in the sensations of pain, temperature, touch and pressure;

2. Proprioceptors in muscles, tendons and joints which provide data for reflex adjustments of muscle action and for the awareness of position and movement;

3. Interoceptors in the viscera. The sensation carried from these receptors is less precisely localised than that mediated by the other two classes. (See Chapter VI).

The sensory endings are supplied by nerve fibres which vary in size and in other characteristics. The actual endings may be primitive and unencapsulated or phylogenetically more recent and therefore specialised and encapsulated. The neuromuscular spindles are the most complicated of the receptors and are important for the control of muscle tension.

The dorsal root ganglia are present on the dorsal roots of the spinal nerves proximal to the formation of the definitive spinal nerves. These ganglia contain the cell bodies of primary sensory neurons which have developed from the neural crest cells. The primary sensory neurons are originally bipolar but the two processes unite to form a single process and this fibre divides into a central and a peripheral branch. The peripheral branch terminates in a sensory ending and the central branch enters the spinal cord through the dorsal nerve root. Both the central and the peripheral branches have the characteristics of an axon although one is acting as a dendrite in terms of conduction towards the cell body. Note that there are no synapses in the dorsal root ganglia.

There are two main categories of efferent or motor neurons:

1. *Somatic efferent neurons*—These are situated in the anterior grey horns of the spinal cord and the fibres pass through the ventral roots of the spinal nerves to terminate on motor end plates in the skeletal muscle fibres. This pathway is called the 'final common pathway' to skeletal muscle because the anterior horn cells receive information from descending tracts and from cells acting as links in reflex circuits so that the character of any movement has been determined by this interaction of impulses terminating on the anterior horn cells. The motor end plates in voluntary muscles are made up of a motor nerve fibre and part of the underlying muscle. A 'motor-unit' consists of the nerve fibre of a motor neuron and the muscle fibres innervated by that

neuron. Every muscle fibre has a motor end plate and therefore has a branch of an efferent nerve fibre associated with it.

2. *Visceral efferent neurons*—Here we are considering the autonomic nervous system and it has a special feature in that it is a two-neuron pathway from the central nervous system to the viscera. An example of visceral efferent neurons is to be found in the sympathetic system where the first neuron is located in the thoracic or upper lumbar region of the spinal cord. The axons leave the central nervous system via the ventral root of the spinal nerve and leave the spinal nerve via the white ramus communicans to end in a ganglion. There is a synapse in the ganglion and the postganglionic fibre may pass onwards to a viscus or may return via the grey ramus communicans to be distributed along the course of the nerve. In some circumstances the fibre going to

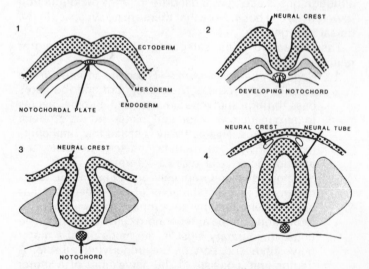

Fig. 3. Development of the neural tube.

a viscus passes through the ganglion without synapsing to form the splanchnic nerves which have their ganglia in the median plane.

Postganglionic autonomic endings on smooth muscle and secretory cells are similar to synapses. The fine axons make contact with the effector cell and there is frequently a swelling along the course of the axon or at its end which fits into a depression on the surface of the muscle or gland cell. The ganglia of the efferent system, that is, the sympathetic and parasympathetic ganglia are the situations where the fibre of the preganglionic cell synapses with the cell body of the postganglionic nerve cell.

Development

Figure 3 shows the development of the neural tube which begins to form at the end of the third week of gestation by a midline invagination of the dorsal ectoderm. The ectoderm thickens to form the neural plate and then becomes invaginated to form the neural groove. Eventually, the invaginated ectoderm becomes separated from the surface ectoderm and a tube is formed. Closure of the neural tube starts in the thoracic region and progresses rostrally and caudally.

The lateral margins of the neural plate (neural crest cells) are continuous with the general body ectoderm and these margins are approximated as the neural tube is formed. Neural crest cells form a temporary layer between the neural tube and the surface ectoderm but finally migrate laterally. The groups of neural crest cells give rise to the dorsal root ganglia of the spinal nerves and similar groups of cells in the brain give rise to the ganglia of some of the cranial nerves. The neural crest cells migrate widely and are the origins of most of the sensory cells and fibres of the peripheral nervous system, the Schwann cell sheath of all peripheral nerves, satellite cells in ganglia, sympathetic ganglia, chromaffin cells and pigment cells.

The neural tube has a lumen and the lumen persisting in the spinal cord is called the central canal of the spinal cord. The expanded lumen of the original tube in the brain forms the ventricular system.

Growth and differentiation of the neural tube is greatest in the rostral portion from which the brain develops. Three swellings, the primary brain vesicles, appear at the rostral end of the neural tube at the end of the fourth week of gestation. The primary brain vesicles are the prosencephalon (forebrain), the mesencephalon (midbrain) and the rhomb-encephalon (hindbrain). The caudal and rostral brain vesicles each divide into two swellings during the fifth week of gestation. This results in five secondary brain vesicles which are called the telencephalon, diencephalon, mesencephalon (identical to the primary mesencephalon), metencephalon and myelencephalon. The secondary vesicles of the embryonic brain are a commonly used frame of reference for description and analysis of the adult brain although the boundaries between the secondary brain vesicles have been obscured by growth.

Figure 4 depicts the developing brain. Mechanical factors are important determinants in the development of the final adult form of the brain. At the fifth to sixth weeks of gestation an imbalance occurs so that there is a dis-crepancy between the rate of neural expansion and the available space. This imbalance manifests itself by the formation of flexures in the originally straight neural tube. One flexure, the mesencephalic flexure, persists in the adult and its persistence explains the fact that in the adult the telencephalon and diencephalon are aligned at right angles to the longitudinal axis of the brain stem. The telencephalon grows laterally as well as expanding and it begins to cover the diencephalon so that in the adult the diencephalon is completely covered by derivatives of the telencephalon.

The ventricular system is the expanded rostral end of the lumen of the neural tube. It is shown in the developing brain in Figure 5. Caudally the ventricular system is con-tinuous with the central canal of the spinal cord at the caudal border of the medulla oblongata. Traced rostrally the ventricular system expands to form the fourth ventricle

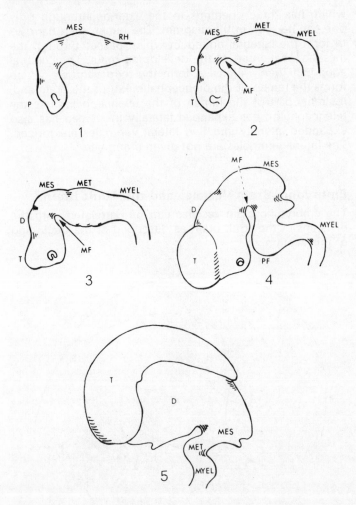

Fig. 4. The developing brain. P=prosencephalon; MES=mesen-
cephalon; RH=rhombencephalon; D=diencephalon; T=telen-
cephalon;   MET=metencephalon;   MYEL=myelencephalon;
MF=mesencephalic flexure; PF=pontine flexure.

which has three openings to the exterior although only one can be seen in the diagram. The lumen then narrows to form the cerebral aqueduct which passes through the mesencephalic part of the developing brain. The cerebral aqueduct then widens to form the third ventricle which forms the lumen of the diencephalic part of the brain and, rostrally, part of the lumen of the telencephalon. As the telencephalon has expanded laterally the lumen has also expanded laterally and two lateral ventricles are formed. The lateral ventricles are not given a number.

Embryonic Brain Vesicles and the Adult Brain

The embryonic brain vesicles can be correlated with the divisions of the adult brain as described at the beginning of this section.

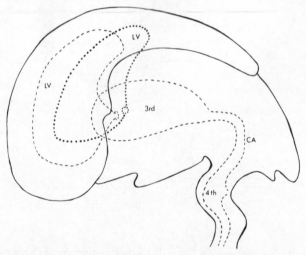

Fig. 5. The developing brain with the ventricular system. LV= lateral ventricle; 3rd=third ventricle; CA=cerebral aqueduct; 4th=fourth ventricle.

The forebrain is composed of the telencephalon, from which the cerebral hemispheres are formed, and the diencephalon which forms the part of the brain lying between the cerebral hemispheres.

The midbrain is derived from the mesencephalon.

The hindbrain is divided into the cerebellum, pons and medulla oblongata. The cerebellum and pons develop from the metencephalon and the medulla oblongata develops from the myelencephalon.

CHAPTER II

THE SPINAL CORD:
GENERAL TOPOGRAPHY

Development

The central nervous system is divided into two major parts, the brain and the spinal cord. The spinal cord or spinal medulla is the least modified part of the central nervous system and can therefore be used to examine fundamental organisation. Initially, it is an unsegmented tube but as the mesoderm segments lateral to the neural tube a segmentation of the myelon (embryonic spinal cord) occurs. For each somite there is a spinal cord segment or NEURO-MERE. Each neuromere gives rise to a pair of spinal nerves. The original relationship between neuromere and somite remains apparent in the adult through strips of cutaneous innervation called DERMATOMES. Clinically, a knowledge of the area of skin supplied by each spinal nerve is very helpful in the diagnosis of the level of suspected damage of the spinal cord.

During development a bilateral longitudinal furrow appears along the inner, luminal surface of the neural tube in the coronal plane. Figure 6 shows the furrow which is called the sulcus limitans. The sulcus limitans extends along the length of the myelon and continues into the brain stem. The dotted lines extending laterally from the sulcus limitans divide the myelon into a dorsal (posterior) part and a ventral (anterior) part and demarcate functional areas of the future spinal cord. The posterior part comprises the ALAR LAMINAE or plates and will be associated with sensation and so may be designated the afferent part of the future spinal cord. The

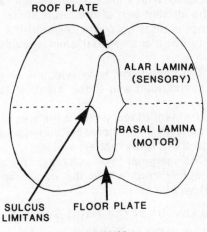

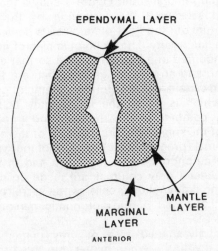

Fig. 6. The developing neural tube.

anterior part comprises the BASAL LAMINAE or plates and it will be associated with motor activities and so may be designated the efferent part of the future spinal cord. Also seen is the roof plate lying posteriorly and the floor plate lying anteriorly. The alar and basal laminae divide into three layers:

Layer 1—The ependymal layer which lines the central canal in the adult and is the germinal layer in the embryo;

Layer 2—The mantle layer which is the area of the future spinal cord where the nerve cell bodies and processes close to them (grey matter) will lie;

Layer 3—The marginal layer which is the area of the future spinal cord where the nerve fibres (white matter) will lie.

The General Layout of the Adult Spinal Cord

The relationships of the grey and white matter in the adult spinal cord correspond to the basic layout of the layers of the developing neural tube. Figure 7 shows that the roof plate disappears with the formation of the posterior median septum but the floor plate persists posterior to the anterior median fissure. The embryonic plan of grey matter becomes modified to a butterfly shape so that a posterior grey column and an anterior grey column are formed on each side. In certain regions a further column of grey matter develops which is called the lateral grey column. The lateral grey columns in the thoracic and upper lumbar segments of the spinal cord are made up of the cell bodies of the proximal (preganglionic) neurons of the sympathetic part of the autonomic nervous system and in the sacral region the lateral grey columns are made up of the cell bodies of the preganglionic cells of the sacral part of the parasympathetic part of the autonomic nervous system (see Chapter I).

The butterfly-shaped area of grey matter makes it possible to divide the white matter into three regions on each side. These three regions are called the posterior,

GENERAL

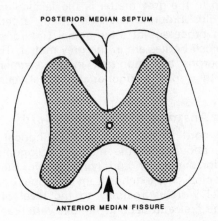

T1–L2

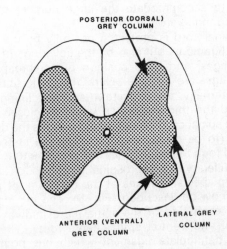

Fig. 7. The spinal cord in transverse section.

lateral and anterior white columns or funiculi. The part of each white column or funiculus which is in immediate relationship to the grey matter is the fasciculus proprius. The fasciculus proprius is made up of ascending and descending processes of internuncial (interposed) neurons whose cell bodies are in the grey matter. These internuncial neurons are important in intersegmental reflex arcs since they form a functional link between adjacent segments.

The Gross Anatomy of the Spinal Cord

The spinal cord in the adult is a cylindrical structure, continuous above with the medulla oblongata, slightly flattened dorsoventrally and lying within the vertebral canal. The spinal cord extends from the upper border of the first cervical vertebra rostrally to the level of the disc between the first and second lumbar vertebrae caudally. It shows two expansions, one in the cervical region and one in the lumbar region. These expansions are necessary in order to accommodate the large number of neurons required to innervate the limbs.

The spinal cord is protected not only by the vertebrae and their ligaments but also by the coverings of the cord, the meninges, and by a cushion of cerebrospinal fluid. The meninges are in three layers, the thick, fibrous DURA MATER externally, the delicate ARACHNOID lining the dura mater and the thin PIA MATER which is closely wrapped round the spinal cord except where it forms the denticulate ligament (to be discussed later). The pia mater and the arachnoid form the boundaries of the SUBARACHNOID SPACE which is filled with cerebrospinal fluid.

The two special features of the pia mater of the spinal cord can now be described (Fig. 8). The pia mater forms ridges on each side of the spinal cord midway between the dorsal and ventral spinal nerve roots. These ridges form the denticulate ligament which has pointed parts which pierce the arachnoid and become attached to the inner surface of the dura mater. Twenty-one

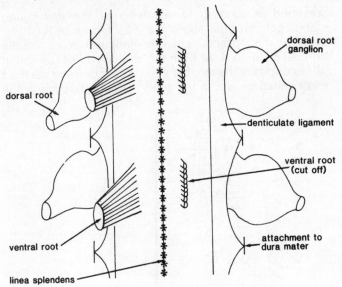

Fig. 8. Spinal pia mater.

points or teeth are present on each side of the spinal cord and the processes are attached to the dural sheath at intervals between the foramen magnum and the level at which the dura mater is pierced by the first lumbar spinal nerve. The second special feature of the pia mater of the spinal cord is that the pia is thickened in such a way anteriorly that it fills up the anterior median fissure. This gives a glistening appearance in the midline of the spinal cord anteriorly and the shining line is called the linea splendens.

The arachnoid shows no particular features. The dura mater is surrounded by a layer of extradural fat and sleeves of dura mater cover the roots of the spinal nerves and terminate by becoming attached to the boundaries of the inter-vertebral foramina.

The spinal cord does not fill the whole length of the vertebral canal in the adult. Segments of the neural tube correspond in position to segments of the developing vertebral column until about the third month of fetal life. Thereafter the vertebral column elongates more rapidly than the spinal cord. At birth the caudal end of the spinal cord lies opposite the disc between the second and the third lumbar vertebrae and in the adult the cord extends to the

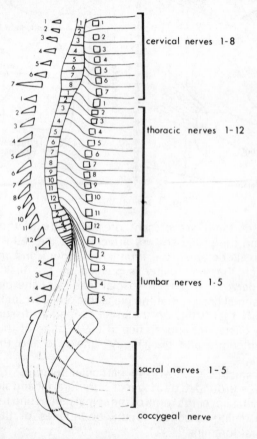

cervical nerves 1-8

thoracic nerves 1-12

lumbar nerves 1-5

sacral nerves 1-5

coccygeal nerve

Fig. 9. Relation of segments of the spinal cord and the spinal nerves to the vertebral column.

disc between the first and second lumbar vertebrae. Clearly, the spinal cord segments in the adult do not correspond to the vertebral levels. It is usual to localise the spinal segments in terms of the palpable parts of the vertebrae, that is, the spinous processes. Figure 9 shows that the nerve roots, which passed almost horizontally in the embryo, retain this arrangement in the upper cervical region only and all the other nerve roots descend for increasing distances before they reach their appropriate exit from the vertebral canal. The lower lumbar, sacral and coccygeal nerve roots descend almost vertically and constitute the cauda equina which surrounds the tapering lower extremity of the spinal cord which is called the filum terminale.

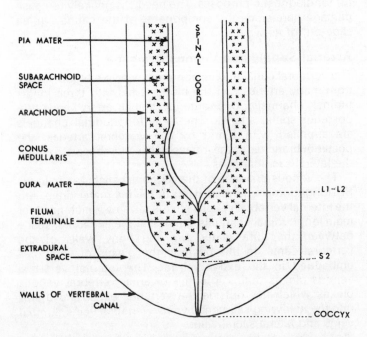

Fig. 10. Caudal end of spinal cord; coronal section.

The arrangement of the meninges at the caudal end of the spinal cord is of great importance clinically (Fig. 10). The conical termination of the spinal cord is the conus medullaris and it is prolonged caudally as the filum terminale which is attached to the coccyx inferiorly. The pia mater closely invests the spinal cord except where it forms the denticulate ligament as explained above. The subarachnoid space is very large from the level of the disc between the first and second lumbar vertebrae to the second piece of the sacrum. Passing through this lumbar sac or theca is the leash of nerve roots forming the cauda equina. The lumbar sac provides a means of obtaining a sample of cerebrospinal fluid. A needle is introduced into the subarachnoid space of the spinal theca and cerebrospinal fluid can be drawn off for diagnostic purposes. The needle is unlikely to cause damage here since the components of the cauda equina slide out of its way.

Arterial Supply and Venous Drainage

The vertebral canal and its contents receive a blood supply from many arteries and the blood is fed into three longitudinal channels, one anterior spinal artery and two posterior spinal arteries. The three longitudinal channels are supplied with blood by the vertebral arteries, the posterior branches of the intercostal and lumbar arteries and the lateral sacral arteries.

The venous drainage of the vertebral canal is as follows. Six longitudinal channels lying in the pia mater drain into the internal vertebral venous plexus of veins which has four main longitudinal channels situated in the extradural space between the dura mater and the bony walls of the vertebral canal. In this position the plexus of veins lies embedded in the extradural fat. The internal vertebral venous plexus drains into the external vertebral venous plexus which lies outside the vertebral canal and drains into the following segmental veins: vertebral veins; lumbar veins and lateral sacral veins.

CHAPTER III

THE BRAIN:
GENERAL TOPOGRAPHY

The Position of the Brain in the Skull

The brain is divided into three parts. The brain stem, continuous inferiorly with the spinal cord, the cerebellum and the cerebral hemispheres and the part lying between them. The brain is enclosed within the skull which has (1) a box to contain the brain made up of a thick base and a vault and (2) the facial skeleton which has an upper part fixed to the brain box and a lower part which is movable and carries the lower teeth. Figure 11 shows the position of the brain within the skull. The interior of the base of the skull has three depressions or fossae which are not at one level but are stepped downwards rostrocaudally. The anterior cranial fossa has the anterior parts of the cerebral hemispheres lying on it. The middle cranial fossa possesses two lateral depressions which receive parts of the cerebral hemispheres and a central depression which houses the pituitary gland (hypophysis cerebri). The posterior cranial fossa is the most inferior; in the median part of its anterior region lies the brain stem, and the remainder of the fossa is occupied by the cerebellum. The medulla oblongata emerges through the foramen magnum of the skull and becomes continuous with the spinal cord at the upper border of the first cervical vertebra.

The Brain Stem and the Cranial Nerves

The brain stem is divided caudorostrally into the medulla oblongata, pons and midbrain. Figure 12 shows the brain

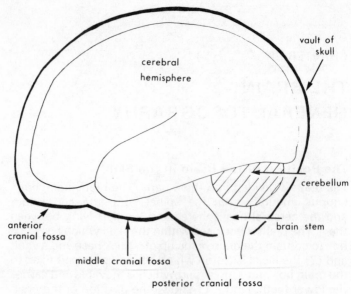

Fig. 11. Diagram showing position of brain in skull.

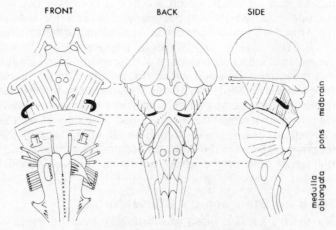

Fig. 12. Brain stem; gross anatomy.

stem in three views. The terms 'front' and 'back' are not strict anatomical terms. The so-called 'front' view of the brain stem and related structures can be appreciated from Figure 13. There is a flexure at the level of the midbrain due to mechanical factors in development. When looking at the

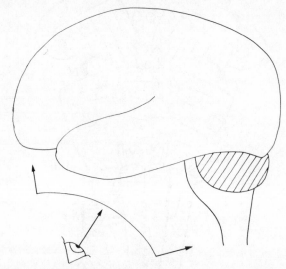

Fig. 13. Field of view when looking at 'front' of brain stem.

'front' of the brain stem it has to be appreciated that the view is of the field indicated by the arrows, i.e. the flexure has been straightened and the whole arc of view is seen as if it were in one plane.

Figure 14 shows the 'front' of the brain stem as previously defined with some of the cranial nerves. Caudally is the medulla oblongata with a median fissure, on either side of which is an elevation called the pyramid; lateral to the upper part of each pyramid is an elevation, the olive, the left one of which is partially covered by the hypoglossal (XIIth) nerve in the diagram. Lying rostral to the medulla oblongata is the pons which shows in this view a mass of

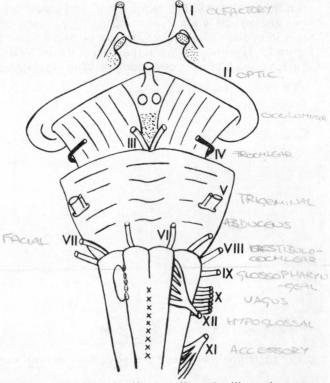

Fig. 14. Brain stem; front. I=olfactory; II=optic; III=oculomotor; IV=trochlear; V=trigeminal; VI=abducent; VII=facial; VIII=vestibulocochlear; IX=glossopharyngeal; X=vagus; XI=accessory; XII=hypoglossal.

fibres running transversely with a median groove. Rostral to the pons is the midbrain which shows the massive cerebral peduncles (the stalks of the cerebral hemispheres) which are superficially composed of descending tracts connecting the cerebral hemispheres with the pons and spinal cord, and lying between the cerebral peduncles are the mamillary bodies (caudal) and the stalk or infundibulum of the hypophysis cerebri (rostral).

All or parts of the cranial nerves or tracts of the cranial nerves can be seen in the 'front' view of the brain stem. There are twelve pairs of cranial nerves which are given Roman numerals as well as names.

I   *The olfactory nerves*—The structure labelled I in Figure 14 is the left olfactory tract which has had its rostral extremity cut off. The actual olfactory nerves, which are concerned with the sense of smell, lie in the roof of the nasal cavity and terminate in the olfactory bulb. The olfactory bulb is continuous with the olfactory tract which splits into medial and lateral parts as it passes caudally.

II *The optic nerves*—The structure labelled II in Figure 14 is the left optic tract. The optic chiasma where some decussation (crossing over of fibres) takes place can be seen. The optic nerves are concerned with vision.

III *The oculomotor nerves;* IV the *trochlear nerves;* and VI the *abducent nerves*. These are grouped together as they innervate the extra-ocular muscles which move the eyeball. The oculomotor nerves emerge at the upper border of the pons medial to the cerebral peduncles, the abducent nerves emerge at the upper border of the pyramids of the medulla oblongata and the trochlear nerves appear in the diagram as they wind round the lateral aspects of the cerebral peduncles. The trochlear nerves are the only cranial nerves which emerge from the dorsal aspect of the brain stem. The oculomotor nerves have parasympathetic fibres in them contributing to the craniosacral outflow of the parasympathetic system (see Chapter I).

V   *The trigeminal nerves*—These nerves are very large and eventually divide into three parts, hence the name. They are concerned with sensation from the major part of the face and scalp and also have a motor division which supplies the muscles of mastication or chewing muscles. They emerge through the substance of the transverse fibres of the pons and their presence is used as a landmark. The structure lying medial to the nerves is the pons itself and the continuation of the pontine fibres laterally forms one of the pair of stalks or peduncles which attach the cerebellum to the remainder of the central nervous system.

VII *The facial nerves*—These nerves are concerned with the innervation of the muscles of facial expression, that is, those muscles which are attached to skin at one end so as to bring about movements of the face as in smiling. The facial nerves have a parasympathetic component.

VIII *The vestibulocochlear nerves*—These are concerned with the transmission of information from the balancing and hearing apparatus, located in the inner ear, to the central nervous system.

IX *The glossopharyngeal nerves*—These nerves have sensory and motor parts and assist in the innervation of the tongue and pharynx. They also contain parasympathetic fibres.

X *The vagus nerves*—The name means 'wanderer' and these nerves supply sensory and motor fibres to certain structures in the neck and to the viscera of the thorax and abdomen. They contain parasympathetic fibres.

XI *The accessory nerves*—There are two parts to these nerves. One part arises in the brain stem and the other part arises in the spinal cord. The spinal divisions of the accessory nerves supply a special group of muscles and the cranial divisions join the vagus nerves and are therefore 'accessory to the vagus'.

XII *The hypoglossal nerves*—These nerves supply motor fibres to the muscles of the tongue.

The 'nerves' that have been described are made up of nerve fibres. The nerve cell bodies lie either within the brain stem as masses called the nuclei of the cranial nerves or in the sensory ganglia of the cranial nerves.

Lying lateral to the optic chiasma is the anterior perforated substance where arteries enter the brain. The hollows lying lateral to the optic chiasma are called the valleculae cerebri and this is a useful term as it is here that one of the two pairs of major arteries supplying the brain can be found. Many small arteries perforate the midbrain in the region of the interpenduncular fossa (the ditch between the two cerebral peduncles) and this region is the posterior perforated substance.

Figure 15 depicts the 'back' of the brain stem. So that the main features can be seen, the stalks or peduncles attaching the cerebellum to the brain stem have been cut and the cerebellum removed. Caudally lies the medulla

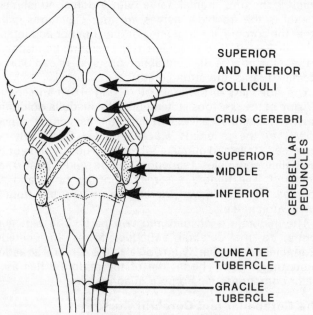

Fig. 15. Brain stem; back.

oblongata and it shows two pairs of elevations. The cuneate tubercles are lying laterally and they extend more rostrally than the gracile tubercles which lie adjacent to the midline. These tubercles mark the end of the posterior white columns of the spinal cord and the elevations are formed because of the presence of groups of nerve cell bodies on which the posterior white columns are terminating. Because the cerebellum has been removed the floor of the fourth ventricle is exposed and it shows two inverted Y-shaped depressions, a bundle of fibres running transversely and two circular elevations lying rostrally to the transversely running fibres.

The dotted areas indicate the cut ends of the three pairs of cerebellar peduncles which are termed superior, middle and inferior. Rostrally is the trochlear (IV) nerve which is the only cranial nerve with a dorsal attachment. Rostral to the trochlear nerves are four elevations called either the corpora quadrigemina or the superior and inferior colliculi. Part of the attachment of the cerebral hemispheres to the remainder of the central nervous system can be seen laterally, that is, the crura cerebri.

The side view of the brain stem (Fig. 16) can serve as revision of the previous statements. The medulla oblongata shows elevations called pyramids on its ventral aspect. Lateral to the pyramids are the olives. Posteriorly are lying the gracile and cuneate tubercles. The cut ends of the cerebellar peduncles (superior, middle and inferior) are indicated. The midbrain is rostral to the pons and the trochlear nerve is shown winding round ventrally from its dorsal attachment.

The midbrain is divided into two parts. The part lying ventral to the cerebral aqueduct forms the cerebral peduncles and the part lying dorsal to the cerebral aqueduct forms the tectum. The tectum of the midbrain has as its major component the corpora quadrigemina.

The Cerebellar and Cerebral Cortex

The hemispheres of the cerebellum and cerebrum develop a

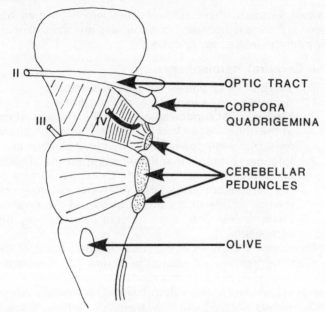

Fig. 16. Brain stem; side.

cortex. In the spinal cord the grey matter is centrally positioned and the white matter lies peripherally. In the cerebellar and cerebral hemispheres migration of nerve cells occurs so that the hemispheres have a layer of grey matter on their surfaces which is called the cortex. Deep masses of grey matter still remain within the hemispheres but there is this additional layer of grey on the surface of the hemispheres.

The cerebellar cortex has the same histological structure in all areas and it has an irregular contour because of many transverse folds or folia. The cerebral cortex shows consistent histological patterns depending on the area and it is assumed that these differences are related to function.

The cortex of the cerebral hemispheres is thrown into folds. The elevations are called gyri (singular, gyrus) and the dips between the elevations are called sulci (singular, sulcus). Some of these sulci and gyri are haphazard but there are certain constant ones which are important as they can be related to function.

The Cerebral Hemispheres

The cerebral hemispheres have three surfaces:

1   Superolateral; a very large, convex surface;
2. Medial; a flat surface adjacent to the medial surface of the opposite cerebral hemisphere although structures intervene between the two medial surfaces;
3. Inferior: an irregular surface resting on the anterior and middle cranial fossae and the upper surface of the cerebellum. Structures intervene between the inferior surface of the posterior part of the cerebral hemispheres and the superior surface of the cerebellum.

The essential features of the superolateral surface of the cerebral hemisphere are shown in Figure 17. The sulcus which can always be found easily in a specimen is the lateral sulcus. The lateral sulcus has a stem rostrally which also extends medially and a posterior ramus directed caudally. Associated with the lateral sulcus are the horizontal and ascending rami. On the superolateral surface is part of the central sulcus and caudally, parts of the calcarine and parieto-occipital sulci. A notch can often be appreciated inferiorly which is called the preoccipital notch. It is customary to divide the cerebral hemispheres into lobes and the method of doing this is rather arbitrary. A line is drawn from the end of the parieto-occipital sulcus to the pre-occipital notch and then a perpendicular is dropped from the end of the posterior ramus of the lateral sulcus to the first line. In this way four lobes are demarcated:

1. The occipital lobe, lying caudally;
2. The parietal lobe, lying superiorly and extending as far forwards as the central sulcus;
3. The frontal lobe, lying rostrally;
4. The temporal lobe, lying inferiorly and resting in the lateral depression of the middle cranial fossa.

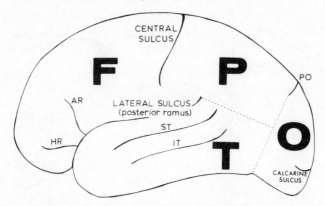

Fig. 17. Cerebral hemispheres; superolateral surface. AR= ascending ramus of lateral sulcus; HR=horizontal ramus of lateral sulcus; ST=superior temporal sulcus; IT=inferior temporal sulcus; PO=parieto-occipital sulcus.

The above terminology relates the cerebral hemispheres to the bones of the skull.

The medial surface of one hemisphere is separated from the medial surface of the other hemisphere by the longitudinal fissure. In the inferior part of this fissure is a mass of white fibres which connects the two hemispheres and which has been cut through in order to separate the two hemispheres and expose the medial surface. Figure 18 shows the medial surface of a cerebral hemisphere with the mass of white fibres cut through. The mass of white fibres is the corpus callosum. In a caudal position are the parieto-occipital and calcarine sulci. Superiorly is the central sulcus and in addition there is the cingulate sulcus which follows the line of the corpus callosum. The area of cortex described as the paracentral lobule is most important as it has to do with sphincter control.

The inferior surfaces of the cerebral hemispheres are shown in Fig. 19. Recall that although they appear to be in one plane they are in fact stepped to conform with the **superior surfaces of the base of the skull. The main features**

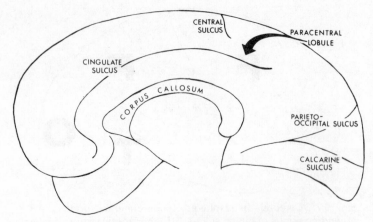

Fig. 18. Cerebral hemispheres; medial surface.

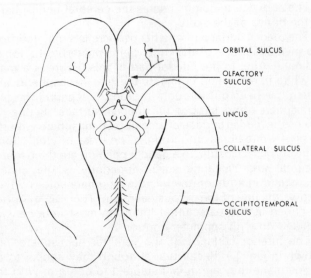

Fig. 19. Cerebral hemispheres; inferior surface.

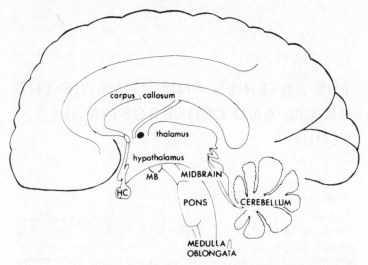

Fig. 20. The brain; median sagittal section. HC = hypophysis cerebri; MB = mamillary body.

close to the midline are the olfactory bulbs and tracts, the optic chiasma, the stalk of the pituitary gland, the mamillary bodies and the cut end of the brain stem. The sulci to be noted on the inferior surfaces of the frontal lobes are the olfactory and orbital sulci. Posteriorly, the named sulci are the collateral and the occipito-temporal. The area of cortex which has a name to be memorised is lateral to the mamillary bodies and is called the uncus because of its supposed resemblance to a hook.

Median Sagittal Section of the Brain

Figure 20 is a median sagittal section of the brain showing the relative sizes and positions of the parts.

CHAPTER IV

THE ARTERIES AND VEINS OF THE BRAIN, AND CEREBROSPINAL FLUID

The Arteries of the Brain

The brain represents 2 per cent of the body weight but receives 16.6 per cent of the total cardiac output. The blood supply to the brain is from the two vertebral arteries and the two internal carotid arteries. The internal carotid arteries are terminal branches of the two common carotid arteries and enter the skull through the carotid canals. The vertebral arteries are branches of the subclavian arteries and enter the skull through the foramen magnum having previously passed through the successive foramina of the transverse processes of the upper six cervical vertebrae.

Figure 21 shows the general disposition of the arteries on the ventral aspect of the brain stem and the inferior surfaces of the cerebral hemispheres.

The vertebral arteries cross the posterior arch of the atlas superiorly, pierce the dura mater and wind round onto the ventral aspect of the brain stem. They terminate by joining the artery of the opposite side at the lower border of the pons to form the basilar artery which occupies the groove on the ventral aspect of the pons. Each vertebral artery has the following branches:

1. The posterior spinal artery;
2. The posterior inferior cerebellar artery, which usually has a loop as shown;

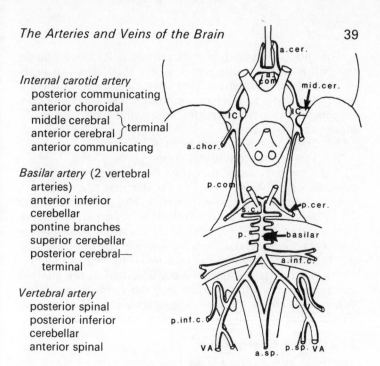

Internal carotid artery
  posterior communicating
  anterior choroidal
  middle cerebral ⎱ terminal
  anterior cerebral ⎰
  anterior communicating

Basilar artery (2 vertebral arteries)
  anterior inferior cerebellar
  pontine branches
  superior cerebellar
  posterior cerebral— terminal

Vertebral artery
  posterior spinal
  posterior inferior cerebellar
  anterior spinal

Fig. 21. Cerebral arteries.

3. The anterior spinal artery which joins with its fellow of the opposite side to form one longitudinal channel anteriorly.

The basilar artery terminates by dividing into the two posterior cerebral arteries rostral to the upper border of the pons; these two arteries wind round the third cranial nerves before passing laterally. The basilar artery has the following branches:

1. The anterior inferior cerebellar artery from which the labyrinthine artery to the inner ear usually arises;

2. The pontine branches which are small and supply the pons;

3. The superior cerebellar arteries which arise at the rostral border of the pons, near the termination of the basilar artery.

The internal carotid arteries pursue a tortuous course through a special bony canal in the skull. The cut ends can be seen in the diagram lying lateral to the optic chiasma and in this region they lie in hollows called the valleculae cerebri. Each internal carotid artery gives off two small branches:

1.   The posterior communicating artery;
2.   The anterior choroidal artery.

After the two small branches have arisen the internal carotid artery divides into its two terminal branches, the anterior and middle cerebral arteries. The anterior cerebral artery bends sharply upwards into the longitudinal fissure between the medial surfaces of the cerebral hemispheres where it communicates with the artery of the opposite side via the anterior communicating artery. The middle cerebral artery is, from its position, the continuation of the internal carotid artery; it runs laterally into the stem of the lateral sulcus. Particulate matter in the internal carotid artery will almost invariably pass into the middle cerebral artery.

The Circulus Arteriosus

The four arteries supplying the brain have formed an arterial circle composed of the posterior cerebral, posterior communicating, anterior cerebral and anterior communicating arteries. Two types of branches arise from the circle and its major branches, these are called the central and the cortical branches. The central branches are slender, arise in groups and pierce the surface of the brain to supply its internal parts. The central branches do not anastomose to any significant extent in the brain substance. The cortical branches spread over the surface of the cortex and anastomose freely in the pia mater and then give rise to small arteries which enter the brain substance in which they do not anastomose.

The area of cerebral cortex supplied by the cortical branches of each of the main cerebral arteries is indicated in Figure 22. The middle cerebral artery supplies most of the superolateral surface of the cerebral hemisphere and contributes only a small amount of blood supply to the medial surface. The anterior and posterior cerebral arteries supply most of the medial surfaces of the cerebral hemispheres and contribute a small amount of blood supply to the superolateral surfaces. All three main arteries supply the inferior surfaces of the cerebral hemispheres, the posterior cerebral arteries being most involved. The distribution of blood to the cerebral cortex from the three pairs of main cerebral arteries must eventually be related to the functional areas of the cortex.

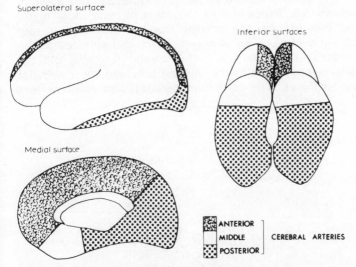

Superolateral surface

Inferior surfaces

Medial surface

ANTERIOR
MIDDLE   CEREBRAL ARTERIES
POSTERIOR

Fig. 22. Cortical distribution of main arteries.

The Venous Drainage of the Brain

The venous drainage of the brain follows the same plan as the arteries as far rostrally as the posterior cerebral artery, that is, the names of the veins correspond to the names of the arteries. The venous drainage more rostrally than the posterior cerebral arteries is complicated by the different arrangement of the dura mater in the cranial cavity as compared with the arrangement for the spinal cord. In the cranial cavity there are two layers of dura mater, an inner and an outer layer. The inner layer is continuous with the dura mater covering the spinal cord and may be termed 'true' dura mater. The outer layer is the internal periosteum of the skull bones. These two layers are firmly united over most of their extent, being separated only where venous channels lie between them or where the 'true' dura mater is infolded to form septa which project between major portions of the brain.

The dural folds are shown in Figure 23. The diagram shows the disposition of the folds of 'true' dura mater to the left of the median sagittal plane. The fold in the midline, lying between the medial surfaces of the cerebral hemispheres, is the falx cerebri. A smaller fold, the falx cerebelli, lies in the midline between the cerebellar hemispheres. The tentorium cerebelli lies more or less

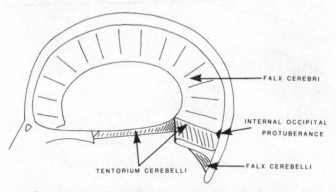

Fig. 23. Dural folds (left of median sagittal plane).

horizontally, separating the inferior surfaces of the posterior lobes of the cerebral hemispheres from the superior surfaces of the cerebellar hemispheres. The tentorium cerebelli roofs over the posterior cranial fossa. The falx cerebri and the falx cerebelli meet the tentorium cerebelli and the posterior extremity of this attachment is marked on the skull by the internal occipital protuberance. The tentorium cerebelli has a free border anteriorly which bounds an aperture occupied by the midbrain. The anterior margin of the tentorium cerebelli is called the tentorial notch. Some of the major venous sinuses in the skull are located within the folds of 'true' dura mater and some are located where these folds turn away from the interior surface of the skull.

The falx cerebri encloses three venous sinuses (Fig. 24) along its borders:

1. The superior sagittal sinus in its fixed margin;
2. The inferior sagittal sinus in its free margin;
3. The straight sinus in its attachment to the tentorium cerebelli.

The superior sagittal sinus begins anteriorly at the crista galli of the skull and runs posteriorly to become continuous with the right transverse sinus at the internal occipital protuberance. The superior cerebral veins drain into this sinus. The superior sagittal sinus has lateral extensions called the lacunae laterales into which the meningeal and diploic veins drain. The diploic veins lie in the diploë of the cranial vault which is the area of trabecular bone situated between inner and outer layers of compact bone.

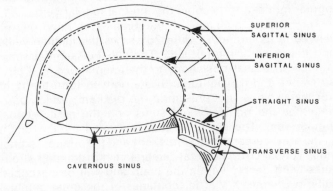

Fig. 24. Veins of the dural folds.

The inferior sagittal sinus is enclosed in the posterior two-thirds of the free margin of the falx cerebri. It drains the falx and part of the medial surfaces of the cerebral hemispheres into the straight sinus.

The straight sinus is formed by the union of the great cerebral vein and the inferior sagittal sinus at the meeting point of the free edges of the falx cerebri and the tentorium cerebelli. It runs postero-inferiorly in the line of union of the two folds. At the internal occipital protuberance the straight sinus becomes continuous with the left transverse sinus.

At the internal occipital protuberance four sinuses are meeting, the straight sinus, the superior sagittal and the right and left transverse sinuses. Often there is a connection between the right and left transverse sinuses; however, the term 'the confluence of the sinuses' is not applied to this connection but to the expanded, posterior end of the superior sagittal sinus.

The transverse sinus is paired and is the widest of all the sinuses. It runs horizontally from the internal occipital protuberance to the base of the petrous temporal bone, lying in the fixed margin of the tentorium cerebelli. Anteriorly the transverse sinus is continuous with the sigmoid sinus which takes an S-shaped course and enters the jugular foramen to become the internal jugular vein.

The venous drainage of the brain will now be reviewed in its entirety. Figure 25 shows the midline veins and the veins of the left side. The superior sagittal sinus (unpaired) passes posteriorly to the internal occipital protuberance and usually turns to the right to form the right transverse sinus (not present in the diagram) which continues as the right sigmoid sinus and the right internal jugular vein. The straight sinus is formed by the union of the great cerebral vein (unpaired) and the inferior sagittal sinus (unpaired). The great cerebral vein is draining structures lying deeply within the brain and will be described fully in Chapter XIV. The tributaries of the great cerebral vein are the right and left basal veins. Each basal vein is

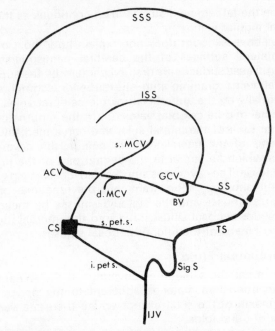

Fig. 25. Midline veins and veins of the left side. (S)=single, (P)=paired. SSS (S)=superior sagittal sinus; ISS (S)=inferior sagittal sinus; SS (S)=straight sinus; TS (P)=transverse sinus; Sig S (P)=sigmoid sinus; IJV (P)=internal jugular vein; CS (P)= cavernous sinus; s.MCV (P)=superficial middle cerebral vein; s.pet.s. (P)=superior petrosal sinus; i.pet.s. (P)=inferior petrosal sinus; ACV (P)=anterior cerebral vein; d.MCV (P)=deep middle cerebral vein; BV (P)=basal vein; GCV (S)=great cerebral vein.

formed deep in the medial part of the stem of the lateral sulcus by the union of the anterior cerebral vein (paired) which runs with the corresponding artery and the deep middle cerebral vein (paired) which lies in the depths of the lateral sulcus accompanied by the middle cerebral artery. The straight sinus runs posteriorly to the internal occipital protuberance and usually turns to the left to become the left sigmoid sinus which continues as the left internal jugular vein.

The above account does not explain how most of the superolateral surfaces of the cerebral hemispheres are drained. These surfaces are drained partially by the superior cerebral veins draining into the superior sagittal sinus and partially by the superficial middle cerebral veins. The superficial middle cerebral veins run in the mouths of the posterior rami of the lateral sulci and curve medially into the stems of the lateral sulci to end in the cavernous sinuses which lie lateral to the central part of the middle cranial fossa. The cavernous sinuses also receive veins from the orbit and they then drain into the junctions of the transverse sinuses and the sigmoid sinuses by means of the superior petrosal sinuses and into the internal jugular veins by means of the inferior petrosal sinuses.

Cerebrospinal Fluid

The brain has the same three coverings as the spinal cord but the 'true' dura mater is adherent to the periosteum of the inside of the skull except where there are venous sinuses or dural folds.

Cerebrospinal fluid is present in the subarachnoid space and the fluid is made in the expanded, rostral end of the original neural tube by structures called choroid plexuses. These are found in the lateral, third and fourth ventricles. In certain places in the ventricular system the ependymal lining comes into contact with the overlying pia mater (Fig 26). The nervous elements of the neural tube are deficient. The choroid plexuses have a folded surface with a central core of connective tissue containing many blood vessels and a surface layer of epithelium. Because of the structure of the epithelium it is clear that the production of cerebrospinal fluid is, at least partly, an active process. The cerebrospinal fluid is clear, colourless and contains small amounts of protein, glucose and potassium and relatively large amounts of sodium chloride. Cerebrospinal fluid is not simply a filtrate of blood plasma as evidenced by its ionic composition and also the osmotic pressure relationships are not suitable to produce from the blood plasma a fluid so deficient in protein.

Cerebrospinal fluid is discharged into the ventricular system and passes out of the system via three foramina

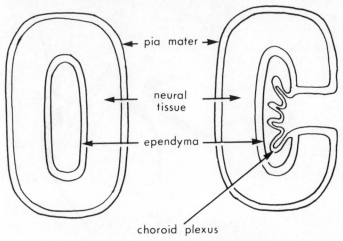

pia mater

neural tissue

ependyma

choroid plexus

Fig. 26. Formation of choroid plexuses.

(one median and two lateral) in the roof of the fourth ventricle into the subarachnoid spaces of the spinal cord and brain.

In places there is a considerable distance between the pia mater and the arachnoid and therefore a large subarachnoid space. These large pools containing cerebrospinal fluid are called cisterns and their position is indicated in Figure 27. There are three major cisterns:

1. The cerebellomedullary cistern. It is sometimes necessary to obtain a sample of cerebrospinal fluid from this cistern in infants as their spinal cords extend further caudally in the vertebral canal than do the spinal cords of adults. The median foramen of the fourth ventricle opens into this cistern.

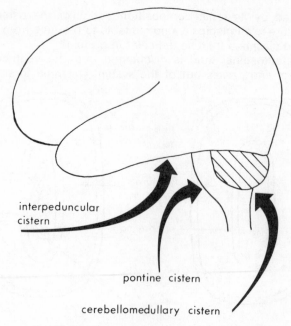

interpeduncular
cistern

pontine cistern

cerebellomedullary cistern

Fig. 27. Positions of cisterns of cerebrospinal fluid.

2. The pontine cistern. This cistern lies on the ventral
    aspect of the pons and the basilar artery lies within
    it. The two lateral foramina of the fourth ventricle
    open into this cistern.
3. The interpeduncular cistern lies between the cere-
    bral peduncles and within this pool of cerebro-
    spinal fluid lies the circulus arteriosus.

The cerebrospinal fluid is made continuously and
therefore it must be absorbed continuously. Resorption
of the cerebrospinal fluid into the venous system occurs
primarily at the arachnoid granulations which are found
mainly associated with the superior sagittal sinus (Fig. 28).
The arachnoid granulations are macroscopic enlargements
of microscopic processes of the arachnoid found in children,

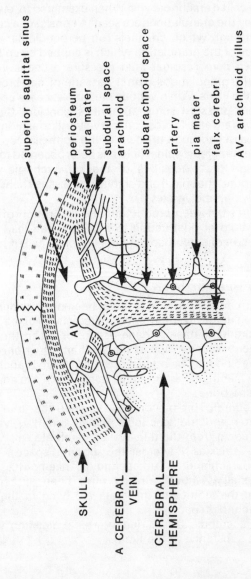

Fig. 28. Coronal section at vertex of skull.

which are called arachnoid villi. When examined by electron microscopy the granulations are seen to consist of a column of cells through which channels run perpendicular to the free surface of the granulation which is capped by epithelial cells. When cerebrospinal fluid pressure exceeds venous pressure the granulations permit passage of cerebrospinal fluid into the veins. When venous pressure exceeds cerebrospinal fluid pressure some authorities consider that the granulations are able to close off in a valve-like fashion. How the fluid passes through the cells of the epithelial cap is not known. Some cerebrospinal fluid has been observed to drain out through the extensions of the subarachnoid space present around the spinal and cranial nerves and thence into adjacent lymphatic vessels.

Imbalance between production and resorption of cerebrospinal fluid or obstruction to free flow can lead to an accumulation of cerebrospinal fluid which is called hydrocephalus.

Cerebral Haemorrhage

There are four main types of cerebral haemorrhage depending on the site of bleeding and the vessels involved:

1. 'Extradural' haemorrhage occurs between the periosteum of the inside of the skull and the bone. This bleeding may be arterial or venous from branches of the meningeal arteries and veins which run adjacent to the bone;

2. Subdural. This bleeding is between the 'true' dura mater and the arachnoid mater and it is venous bleeding from the thin-walled cerebral veins which are at risk as they cross the subdural space;

3. Subarachnoid. Subarachnoid haemorrhage is arterial. It should already have been appreciated that the arteries to the brain are lying in the subarachnoid space.

4. Intracerebral. This is due to arterial bleeding within the substance of the brain.

CHAPTER V

THE NERVE CELL AND NERVE CELL INJURY

General Morphology of the Nerve Cell

The nerve cell (neuron) is a highly differentiated cell which is specialised to propagate a nerve impulse by a combination of electrical and chemical processes. It differs from other cells in that it is unable to undergo cell division in postnatal life.

The study of the neuron using the light microscope requires the use of specific staining procedures for each organelle because of their chemical diversity. In order to visualise the entire nerve cell the observations from several staining methods have to be combined. Electron microscopy and cytochemical techniques have provided more detail of the fine structure and the functions of the organelles. Transmission electron microscopy, being essentially the study of ultrathin sections, makes it difficult to construct the neuron in three dimensions from this data alone. The most unusual feature of the neuron is the presence of protoplasmic processes which may extend for long distances.

The Nerve Cell Body

The nerve cell consists of a nucleus, usually pale-staining, surrounded by a mass of cytoplasm limited by a cell membrane which participates in the reception and transmission of nerve impulses from one cell to another.

The nucleus varies in size from 3 to 18 microns and is usually centrally located except for certain cells in the posterior grey horn of the spinal cord. Some cells of the sympathetic system are binucleate. There is usually one prominent nucleolus. The nucleus and nucleolus of small neurons are small and their chromatin material is rather coarser than that in large neurons.

The cytoplasm shows many features:

1. Nissl granules. In light microscopy the Nissl material appears as clumps of granules and is very basophilic. In electron microscopy the Nissl granules are seen to be a complex of ribosomes studding the endoplasmic reticulum. The Nissl granules are larger in motor than in sensory cells. It is suggested that the Nissl granules are part of the mechanism for the synthesis of cytoplasmic proteins.

2. Neurofibrils. Neurofibrils are found in all nerve cells and the electron microscope shows the neurofibrils seen in light microscopy to be bundles of neurofilaments and neurotubules. The purpose of these structures is not known.

3. Mitochondria. These organelles are scattered throughout the cell body, dendrites and axon. Their most important role is to serve as a source of energy for the cell.

4. The Golgi apparatus (or complex). The Golgi apparatus is highly developed in neurons and, indeed, was first described in nerve cells. The exact role of the Golgi apparatus is not known but its function is thought to be linked to the synthetic mechanisms of the cell.

5. The centrosome. This structure has an important function in the dynamics of mitosis. Adult neurons *in vivo* are incapable of cell division and in such neurons the centrosome is lacking or poorly developed, although during the developmental period a centrosome is present in immature neurons. Paradoxically, it has been found possible to grow adult human sympathetic ganglion cells and cerebral cortex neurons *in vitro* and these cultures have divided mitotically.

6. Pigments. There are two sorts of pigment which may be present as inclusions in the cytoplasm. Melanin is found only in certain areas of the brain and it appears at the end of the first year of life, increases until puberty and thereafter the amount remains constant. Lipofucsin (lipochrome) is a yellowish pigment and the amount increases with age and in senescence it may occupy a large part of the cytoplasm of some neurons. It first appears in the 6th to 8th year of life. It has been suggested that the lipofucsin granules are either derived from or are a form of lysosome.

Dendrites

Dendrites are the afferent processes of central·nervous system neurons and are unmyelinated. In some neurons the smaller branches have numerous short side-branches or spines which are a preferred site of synaptic contact.

Axons

The single axon of a nerve cell tends to have a uniform diameter throughout its length. Axons are the efferent processes of neurons and they may have side-branches or collateral processes. Synaptic vesicles are present at the terminal end and may also be present along the course of some axons (see Synapses below). Vesicles occur at every site where the axon is apposed to a structure to be innervated. Axons within the central nervous system have their myelin coats formed by the oligodendroglia. Axons of the peripheral nervous system have their myelin coats formed by Schwann cells which are derivatives of the neural crest. Not all axons are myelinated but in the peripheral nerves such unmyelinated axons will still possess a Schwann cell lamella.

The peripheral myelinated fibre is the most complicated in structure and it has an axon, myelin and a sheath of Schwann. The myelin coat begins a short distance from the cell body and stops distal to the terminal arborisations

of the axon. The myelin coat is interrupted at regular
intervals and the parts of the fibre where this happens
are known as the nodes of Ranvier. The degree of myelini-
sation depends on the axon diameter with large axons
always having myelin coats and the largest axons possess-
ing the thickest myelin layer.

Synapses

The point of contact of nerve cells where the axon of one
neuron is apposed to the cell body or dendrites of another
neuron or some other effector cell is called a synapse.
There is no cytoplasmic continuity between the two cells
participating in a synapse. The membrane of the axon
terminal (the presynaptic membrane) is separated from
the surface (the postsynaptic membrane) of the neuron
or effector cell by the synaptic cleft. Synaptic vesicles are
abundant in the presynaptic membrane and contain chemi-
cals by means of which transmission across the synapse
is effected.

There are basically three types of synapse in the central
nervous system:

1. Axodendritic; the axon terminates on the dendrite of
    another neuron;
2. Axosomatic; the axon terminates on the cell body of
    another neuron;
3. Axo-axonal; the axon terminates directly on other
    axonic terminals or on the initial segment of the axon
    of another neuron.

Some synapses seem to have a very elaborate structure
involving the processes of astrocytes, the latter isolating
the synapse from the influence of adjacent cells.

Injured Nerve Cells

If the cell body of a nerve cell is damaged then the cell
dies. All the processes degenerate and in a myelinated
axon this happening can be demonstrated by special
staining. Experimentally, it is not yet possible to injure

selectively a single nerve cell body in the central nervous system as other structures are invariably damaged also.

If an axon is damaged there are two results: changes in the parent cell body called the axon reaction and changes in the nerve fibre distal to the injury called Wallerian degeneration.

The axon reaction is a description of the changes which occur in the cell body, these are similar whether the nerve cell involved is in the central or the peripheral nervous system. In man, the typical axon reaction is that the nerve fibre between the lesion and the nerve cell body is not much affected. Twenty-four to forty-eight hours after injury the Nissl granules seem to disappear in a process called chromatolysis, the nucleus becomes eccentric and the cell body swells. Even while these changes take place recovery starts as evidenced by enlargement of the nucleolus, accelerated RNA synthesis and accelerated protein synthesis. The recovery period may extend over several months. In large neurons the reacting cell bodies can be easily identified.

In the central and in the peripheral nervous system the severing of a nerve fibre results in Wallerian degeneration. The axon does not survive long once separated from the parent cell. After 24 hours the axon distal to the lesion becomes swollen and irregular and breaks up into fragments, this process is complete by the 3rd to the 5th day although connective tissue sheaths and other non-nervous components of the nerve fibre remain intact for some time. The myelin coat undergoes complete disintegration and the fragments of myelin take several months to disappear. The final result of Wallerian degeneration depends on whether the fibre is centrally or peripherally located.

It has been found experimentally that one group of degenerating neurons may be followed by similar changes in other neurons on which the degenerating fibres terminate. This is called transneuronal, transsynaptic or postsynaptic degeneration. There is at the moment no explanation for transneuronal degeneration.

Nerve Fibre Regeneration

Regeneration of nerve fibres in the central nervous system is minimal and the affected region is changed into a scar by the activities of the glial cells.

In a severed peripheral nerve, regeneration is possible if the cut ends are approximated surgically. Many fine fibres emerge from the stump of a severed axon, traverse the gap and enter the distal segment. The rate of growth is slow at first and chance plays a large part in the process. Re-myelinisation of the regenerated fibres depends on whether they re-establish contact with the appropriate effector or receptor.

Neuron Tracing Techniques

Nerve cell bodies undergoing axon reaction can be easily identified, so by cutting a nerve fibre the position of the reacting cell body can be established. This method has been used in the brain and spinal cord to discover the source of fasciculi and the cells of origin of fibres in the cranial and spinal nerves. As previously stated, this method is confined to large neurons.

Myelinated fibres can be traced if they undergo Wallerian degeneration by using the Marchi technique in which the chemically altered myelin appears black. This method may be used to study fibre degeneration for many months following an injury. Unmyelinated fibres are traced after degeneration by using silver staining methods. The degenerating fibres can be traced to their synapses because their terminations also have an increased affinity for the silver salt used. Silver staining by the Nauta technique produces precise and detailed information and has been invaluable in the study of the connections in the brain stem and diencephalon.

Radioautography may be used to trace neurons; this involves supplying a radioactive precursor to living tissue which becomes part of the tissue and the location of the radioactivity can be determined by exposing the specimen to a photographic emulsion. If a suitable radioisotopically labelled substance is injected into nervous tissue it is used by the cell bodies to make protein, which is then transported along the axons of the cells to their terminations. The method just described is an orthograde technique. Horseradish peroxidase (HRP) is used as a retrograde technique, i.e. if HRP is injected into the terminal region of an axon it is transported back to the nerve cell body where it can be detected by appropriate staining. The preceding methods are open to misinterpretation.

Other methods have also proved helpful, particularly embryological studies, as different tracts in the central nervous system are myelinated at different stages in development and so pathways can be traced using myelin staining at suitable times.

Biochemical, physiological and pharmacological procedures have been used to trace neurons; e.g. it is possible to block synapses in autonomic ganglia by means of nicotine and observe the result.

CHAPTER VI

GENERAL SENSORY SYSTEMS

The Two Main Sensory Systems

The anatomy of the pathways from general sensation receptors to the thalamus and cerebral cortex where sensation attains a conscious level will be discussed here, and not those pathways which are involved in reflex arcs. The sensory fibres entering the spinal cord via the posterior root segregate in such a way that there are two sensory systems.

System 1 is the phylogenetically older system. The receptor neurons composing it synapse in the posterior grey horn and fibres of the secondary neurons cross to the other side of the spinal cord to continue as the spinothalamic (spine to thalamus) tracts in the lateral and anterior white columns. Pain and temperature sensation ascend in the lateral spinothalamic tracts and coarse (simple) touch ascends in the anterior spinothalamic tracts. Recent physiological work indicates that this sharp division of modalities between the lateral and anterior spinothalamic tracts may be an oversimplification although clinically the division seems to be acceptable. The lateral and anterior spinothalamic tracts are partly protective in function, especially with respect to pain.

System 2 is the phylogenetically more recent pathway. The fibres from the posterior root ganglion of the spinal cord give collaterals to the dorsal grey column and ascend in the ipselateral (same side) posterior white column to end in the nucleus gracilis and nucleus cuneatus of the medulla oblongata. Fibres from the nucleus gracilis and cuneatus cross to the other side of the medulla oblongata to form the medial lemniscus which terminates in the thalamus. This pathway is for proprioception, vibration sense and discriminatory touch. These sensations are closely related to mental activity at the cortical level and emotional responses are minimal.

Three neurons are usually needed to relay sensation from the receptors to the cerebral cortex. The cell bodies of the primary sensory neurons are in the dorsal root ganglia of the spinal nerves and the ganglia of the cranial nerves (mainly the trigeminal nerves). There is one notable exception to this rule which will be described later. The cell bodies lie in the ganglia, their dendrites traverse peripheral or cranial nerves to receptors and their axons enter the spinal cord or brain stem.

The cell bodies of secondary sensory neurons are present: (1) in the grey matter of the spinal cord for the anterior and lateral spinothalamic tracts; (2) in the gracile and cuneate nuclei of the medulla oblongata for the medial lemniscus; and (3) in the sensory trigeminal nuclei for the trigeminothalamic tracts. Tertiary sensory neurons in the thalami project to the sensory cortical areas in the postcentral gyri of the cerebral hemispheres.

The concept of a simple relay along three neurons does not reflect the true situation because small neurons with short axons may be interposed between the major neurons of the pathways.

The Spinal Cord: Posterior Grey Columns

The posterior half of the spinal cord is concerned mainly with sensation. The posterior grey columns are of particular interest in considering the sensory pathways. There are two types of cell to be found in the posterior grey columns: (1) the internuncial cells, and (2) the tract cells.

Internuncial cells (see Chapter II) receive impulses from the dorsal root fibres and their axons are distributed to other cells in the grey matter, particularly the anterior grey horn cells, and therefore they are the intermediate neurons

linking the motor and sensory neurons of the spinal cord
to form spinal reflexes. Some of the axons of internuncial
cells stay within their own spinal segment to form intra-
segmental reflex arcs and some travel rostrally or caudally
to form intersegmental reflex arcs.

Tract cells receive impulses from the dorsal roots and
form tracts which ascend or descend in the posterior
white columns for varying distances, the longest fibres
terminating in the brain. The posterior grey columns can
be subdivided (Fig. 29). The substantia gelatinosa and
the dorsal funicular grey columns form the posterolateral
part of the posterior grey columns and are present throughout the length of the spinal cord. The thoracic nuclei
(Clarke's columns) form the anteromedial part of the
posterior grey columns and extend from the eighth cervical
segment to the third or fourth lumbar segment and the

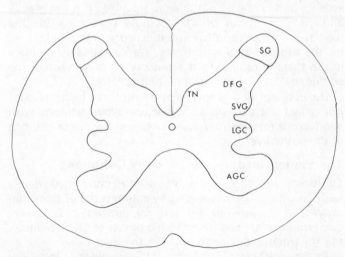

Fig. 29. Transverse section of spinal cord—midthoracic. SG=
substantia gelatinosa; DFG=dorsal funicular grey; TN=thoracic
nucleus; SVG=secondary visceral grey; LGC=lateral grey column;
AGC=anterior grey column.

secondary visceral grey columns lie anterolaterally and extend from the first thoracic segment to the first lumbar segment.

The Spinal Cord: Ascending Tracts for Touch

Figure 30 shows the ascending tracts for both types of touch in the spinal cord. The phylogenetically older system enters by the dorsal root, synapses in the posterior grey horn and crosses to the other side to form the anterior spinothalamic tract which lies in the anterior white column and carries the sensations of coarse touch and pressure. The phylogenetically newer system enters by the dorsal root, sends collaterals into the grey matter and then passes into the posterior white column where it ascends ipselaterally in the fasciculus gracilis or cuneatus of the spinal cord. Fibres arising below the midthoracic region ascend in the fasciculus gracilis and terminate in the nucleus gracilis. Fibres arising above the midthoracic region ascend in the fasciculus cuneatus and terminate in the nucleus cuneatus. The cells of the nucleus gracilis and nucleus cuneatus supply fibres which cross under the central canal to form the internal arcuate fibres or great sensory decussation and these fibres are eventually forming the medial lemniscus.

The important functional difference between the pathway for touch passing rostrally in the posterior white columns and the pathway passing rostrally in the anterior white columns is that the former has a 1 : 1 synaptic ratio so that a stimulated area can be located with precision by the conscious brain and when two points located close to one another are stimulated simultaneously then the brain can appreciate that two areas are being stimulated.

The Spinal Cord: Ascending Tracts for Proprioception

Figure 31 depicts the ascending tracts for proprioception which are especially important in man for learned or skilled motor activities. This modality of sensation provides

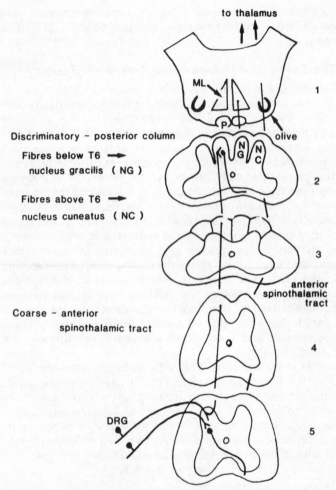

to thalamus

ML

P

olive

Discriminatory – posterior column

Fibres below T6 ➝
 nucleus gracilis (NG)

Fibres above T6 ➝
 nucleus cuneatus (NC)

NG NC

anterior
spinothalamic
tract

Coarse – anterior
 spinothalamic tract

DRG

1
2
3
4
5

Fig. 30. Spinal cord. Ascending tracts–Touch. DRG dorsal (posterior) root ganglion. P pyramid. ML medial lemniscus. 1 open medulla; 2 closed medulla; 3 cervical region; 4 thoracic region; 5 lumbar region.

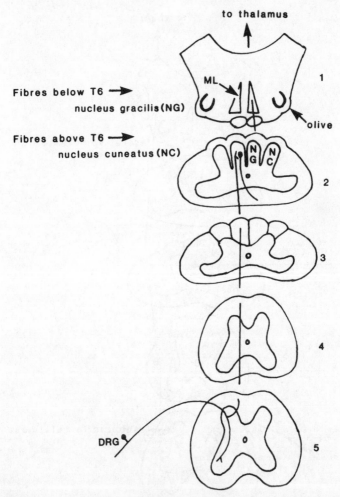

Fig. 31. Spinal cord. Ascending tracts—Proprioception. DRG dorsal (posterior) root ganglion. ML Medial lemniscus. 1 open medulla; 2 closed medulla; 3 cervical region; 4 thoracic region; 5 lumbar region.

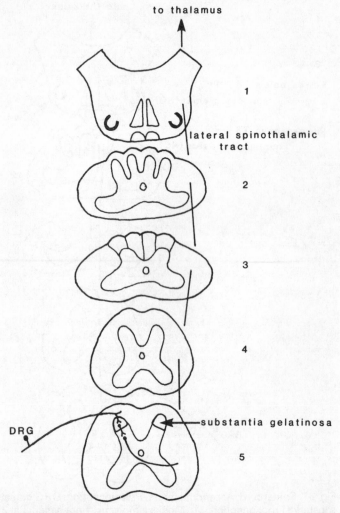

Fig. 32. Spinal cord. Ascending tracts–Pain and temperature. DRG dorsal (posterior) root ganglion. 1 open medulla; 2 closed medulla; 3 cervical region; 4 thoracic region; 5 lumbar region.

awareness of the precise position of body parts, the shape and size of an object held in the hand, weights of objects and the range and direction of movements.

The central processes of the primary sensory neurons enter the spinal cord via the dorsal root and the long ascending fibres travel in the fasciculus gracilis or cuneatus and terminate in the nucleus gracilis or cuneatus. Some collateral fibres terminate in relation to cells in the anterior grey horn and contribute to the formation of proprioceptive spinal reflex arcs. Other collateral fibres synapse on the cells of the thoracic nucleus from which group of cells the posterior spinocerebellar tracts arise.

The Spinal Cord: Ascending Tracts for Pain and Temperature

The fibres which carry pain and temperature sensation (Fig. 32) are smaller and less well myelinated than those concerned with touch and proprioception. The central processes of the cell bodies in the dorsal root ganglia traverse the dorsal roots and enter the dorsolateral fasciculus of Lissauer of the spinal cord in which ascending and descending branches may travel over three segments of the spinal cord before terminating in the substantia gelatinosa of the posterior horn. The dorsolateral tract of Lissauer is posterior to the substantia gelatinosa. It is thought that the cells of the substantia gelatinosa are not tract cells but those of intercalated neurons whose processes synapse with cells in the posterior grey horn, the axons of which cross the midline to form the lateral spinothalamic tract. The lateral spinothalamic tracts continue into the medulla oblongata without appreciable change of position.

The Brain Stem: Course of Sensory Fibres

Figure 33 shows the approximate position of some of the fibres already mentioned, i.e. the medial lemniscus and the anterior and lateral spinothalamic tracts, as they proceed rostrally through the brain stem. The medial lemniscus is

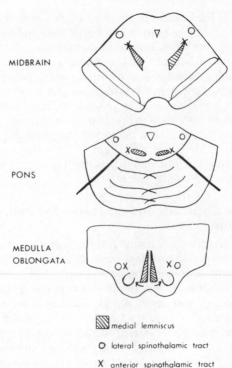

MIDBRAIN

PONS

MEDULLA
OBLONGATA

▨ medial lemniscus

O lateral spinothalamic tract

X anterior spinothalamic tract

Fig. 33. General sensory systems; pathway through brain stem.

lying in close association with the medial lemniscus of
the other side in the medulla oblongata just rostral to the
cuneate and gracile nuclei, but changes this relationship
in the upper part of the medulla oblongata by the swinging
out of its anterior border in the direction indicated by the
arrows. In the pons the medial lemnisci are lying in a
horizontal position with the part originally lying ventral in a
lateral position and the part originally lying dorsal in a
medial position. In the midbrain the medial lemnisci are
lying more laterally and dorsally than they were in the
pons.

The anterior spinothalamic tracts (coarse touch and pressure) are lying close to the lateral borders of the medial lemnisci at the level of the midpons and join the medial lemnisci at the upper border of the pons. The lateral spinothalamic tracts remain as separate entities. All the aforementioned fibres are going to a specific region of the thalami called the ventral nuclei of the thalami.

The Trigeminothalamic Tracts

The cranial nerve most concerned with sensation from the major part of the face and scalp is the trigeminal or fifth cranial nerve. Figure 34 shows the sensory nuclei of the fifth nerve projected onto a diagram of the brain stem. There are three sensory nuclei:

1. The nucleus of the spinal tract of the fifth nerve in the spinal cord, medulla oblongata and pons;
2. The sensory nucleus in the pons;
3. The mesencephalic nucleus of the fifth nerve in the midbrain and rostral pons.

The primary sensory neurons for simple touch, pressure, discriminatory touch, pain and temperature lie in the semi-lunar ganglion of the trigeminal nerve which lies outside the brain and corresponds to the dorsal root ganglion of a spinal nerve. The primary sensory neurons for pro-prioception lie within the mesencephalic nucleus. This is an anomaly as these cells are functionally ganglion cells and should lie outside the central nervous system. All the fibres from the nuclei go to form the trigeminothalamic tract which joins the medial lemniscus. While describing the course of sensory fibres from the spinal cord it has been seen that at some stage a crossing over of fibres from one side to the other takes place. The same phenomenon, that is 'decussation', takes place in the trigeminothalamic tract and the main trigeminal decussation occurs at mid-pons level from fibres arising from the cell bodies of the sensory nucleus of the fifth nerve in the pons.

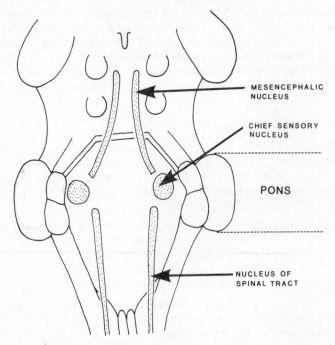

MESENCEPHALIC
NUCLEUS

CHIEF SENSORY
NUCLEUS

PONS

NUCLEUS OF
SPINAL TRACT

Fig. 34. The sensory nuclei of the trigeminal nerve.

The Tracts from the Thalamus to the Cerebral Cortex

All general sensation has to pass to the thalamus and from the thalamus information is projected to the postcentral gyrus of the cerebral cortex. The secondary neuron fibres pass through the tegmentum of the cerebral peduncles, synapse in the thalamus and the tertiary neuron fibres travel in the area of white matter known as the internal capsule (see Chapter XIX) and subsequently spread out to reach the cortex.

The area of cortex to do with sensation is the postcentral

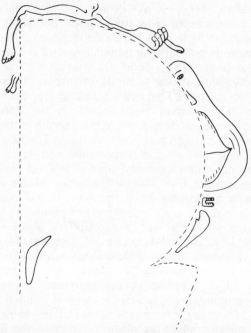

Fig. 35. Sensory homunculus. Postcentral gyrus. (After Penfield, W. and Rasmussen, T. (1950). *The Cerebral Cortex of Man*. New York: Macmillan).

gyrus. Figure 35 shows that the body is represented arching over the hemisphere with the area for the genitals lying on the medial surface of the hemisphere followed by the lower limb, trunk, back of head, upper limb, face, teeth and tongue. The area of cortex designated for each anatomical region is in proportion to the importance of the sensory information from that region.

Sensations from the Viscera

The senses of smell and taste are special visceral sensations, the remaining central input from the viscera consists of general visceral afferents (see Chapter I, Classification of nerve fibres). It will be recalled that the efferent supply to the viscera is by two-neuron pathways termed the parasympathetic and sympathetic parts of the autonomic nervous system. The general visceral afferent fibres use these pathways to send information to the central nervous system but pass without interruption through the autonomic ganglia. The cell bodies of general visceral afferents lie, as would be expected, in the dorsal root ganglia of the spinal nerves and in the ganglia of the cranial nerves which have an autonomic outflow. The two exceptions to this rule are the oculomotor and facial nerves which do not contain general visceral afferent fibres.

The sensations from viscera are rather diffuse as compared with sensations from the rest of the body. The visceral sensations relate to feelings of distension of hollow organs, e.g. stomach, rectum and urinary bladder. In the presence of abnormal function or disease the general visceral afferents carry impulses for pain. The painful sensation is characteristically 'referred' to that part of the body which is supplied by the segmental nerve in the dorsal root ganglion of which the general visceral afferent cells lie. Centrally, the receptive nuclei for somatic and visceral pain impulses are close together in the posterior grey columns of the spinal cord and therefore referred pain is likely to be due to mechanisms within the spinal cord although the precise neurons involved have not been identified. Another explanation is that the constant pain impulses from a disordered viscus lowers the threshold of stimulation of adjacent somatic relay neurons so that normal somatic sensations terminating in the 'excited' neuron pool are misinterpreted as painful stimuli from body surfáces. Some common sites of referred pain are as follows:

Diaphragm referred to dermatome C3 to C5;
Heart referred to dermatomes C8 to T8;
Urinary bladder referred to dermatomes L1, 2 and S2 to S4;
Kidneys referred to dermatomes T10 to T12.

CHAPTER VII

GENERAL MOTOR SYSTEMS

Introduction

The motor systems are the efferent pathways by which means the central nervous system is able to bring about activity in muscles or viscera. The efferent supply of the viscera is via the autonomic nervous system (see Chapter I).

When the centres in the brain initiate movement in muscles descending impulses may reach the muscles by two routes:

1. In the first route impulses pass directly, or through interposed neurons, to the cells of the anterior horn or cranial nerve nuclei and thence to the muscles. Only two neurons are employed (excluding any interposed neuron) and where these two neurons must transmit impulses over the distance between, for example, the cerebral cortex and the foot they will have long axonal processes.
2. The second or indirect route is responsible for the excitation of gamma-efferents which cause contraction of intrafusal muscle fibres within the muscle spindle which in turn cause stretching of the primary sensory endings in the spindle and, via the stretch reflex arc, activation of the main muscle fibres. Delay occurs due to this circuitous route but there is an advantage in that while the muscle is shortening it is under the fine control of the stretch reflex.

The two neurons involved in activating the nerves to the ordinary muscle fibres or to the intrafusal muscle fibres are called the upper and lower motor neurons. The lower motor neurons are the anterior horn cells and their axons which innervate striated muscle but the concept of the lower motor neuron is not confined to the spinal cord. Cells of the motor nuclei of the cranial nerves (III, IV, V, VI, VII, IX, X, XI and XII) which are innervating the muscles of the head and neck are also, functionally, lower motor neurons. The upper motor neurons are the cells which project the motor signal to the effector neurons (lower motor neurons) and their cell bodies are found at higher centres in the brain including the motor cortex and associated areas of the cerebral hemispheres.

Historically, it has been customary to divide the control of somatic muscles into the pyramidal system and the extrapyramidal system. The pyramidal system includes the corticospinal tracts which occupy the pyramids of the medulla oblongata and the corticobulbar tracts which have the same relationship to the motor nuclei of the cranial nerves as the corticospinal tracts have to the anterior horn cells of the spinal cord. The extrapyramidal system consists of all centres and tracts, exclusive of the pyramidal system, which have an influence on the motor cortex or the lower motor neurons. The pyramidal system has, in the past, been equated with the voluntary control of muscle and the extrapyramidal system with smoothing muscle action and antigravity functions. Recent work indicates that the two systems overlap a good deal and the effect of pathological processes in the brain stem and spinal cord of man usually involves the pyramidal and extra-pyramidal systems simultaneously in such a way that the idea of two functionally separate entities is untenable. However, if it is remembered that there is an overlap in the functional sense then the concept of two systems is helpful.

The Overall Plan for Muscle Control

Figure 36 shows a simplified scheme for muscle control. The control of muscles is via the 'final common pathway' of Sherrington in the spinal cord, that is, from the anterior

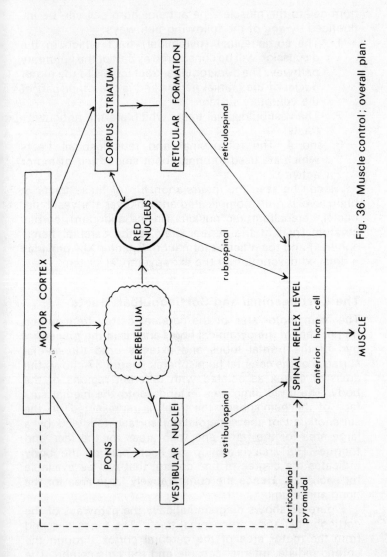

Fig. 36. Muscle control; overall plan.

horn cell to the muscle. The anterior horn cell can be influenced by any of the following pathways:

1. The corticospinal (pyramidal) tract which in the discussion will be considered as part of the voluntary pathway. The corticobulbar tract travels to the motor nuclei of the cranial nerves and is the other part of the voluntary system;

2. The vestibulospinal tracts which are the antigravity tracts;

3. and 4. The rubrospinal and reticulospinal tracts which are used to bring about smoothing of motor activity.

As can be seen the interrelationship of these tracts at brain level is quite complicated and involves the vestibular nuclei, cerebellum, red nucleus (in the midbrain), corpus striatum (part of the central grey of the cerebral hemispheres) and the reticular formation. Chapter XIX provides a detailed description of the extrapyramidal system.

The Corticospinal and Corticobulbar Tracts

The main motor area of the cerebral cortex from which 40 per cent of the pyramidal fibres arise is in the precentral gyri of the frontal lobes and extends onto the medial surfaces of the cerebral hemispheres. Figure 37 shows the areas of cortex associated with different regions of the body. The lower limb area extends onto the medial surface of the hemisphere, the trunk is represented on the superior part of the superolateral surface followed by a large area for the hand and then areas for the face and tongue. The area taken up by each part of the body indicates the degree of fine control that will be available for each part. Hence the comparatively large area for the hand and thumb.

Figure 38 shows diagrammatically the pathways of the corticobulbar and corticospinal tracts. The fibres descend from the motor area of the cerebral cortex through the corona radiata, internal capsule and the crus cerebri. The

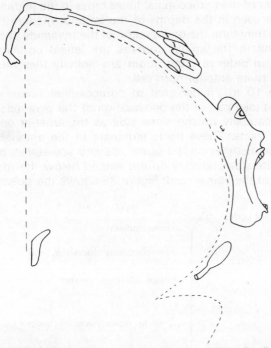

Fig. 37. Motor homunculus. Precentral gyrus. (After Penfield, W. and Rasmussen, T. (1950). *The Cerebral Cortex of Man*. New York: Macmillan.)

crura cerebri are parts of the stalks or peduncles which attach the cerebral hemispheres to the rest of the brain. As the tracts descend through the brain stem fibres leave the main tracts to supply the motor nuclei of the cranial nerves of the other side. The fibres going to the contralateral (other side) nuclei are the corticobulbar tracts. The pyramidal tracts continue caudally and the fibres are grouped together to form two elevations, one on either side of the midline, on the ventral aspect of the medulla oblongata (see Fig. 14). These corticospinal fibres form the pyramids of the medulla oblongata. Eighty to ninety per cent of the corticospinal fibres cross in the midline and can be seen in the depths of the anterior median fissure where they form the decussation of the pyramids and then descend in the spinal cord as the lateral corticospinal tracts. In order to bring about any activity they must be linked to an anterior horn cell.

The 10 to 20 per cent of corticospinal fibres which did not take part in the decussation of the pyramids continue caudally on the same side as the anterior corticospinal tracts. These tracts terminate in the anterior grey horn, sometimes on the same side and sometimes on the opposite side and they do not extend below the thoracic levels of the spinal cord. Figure 39 shows the position of

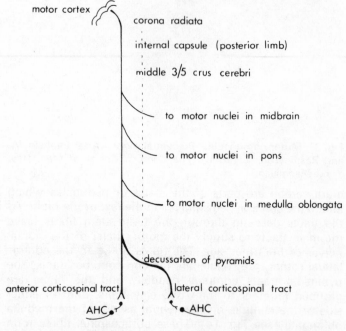

Fig. 38. Corticobulbar and corticospinal (pyramidal) tracts.

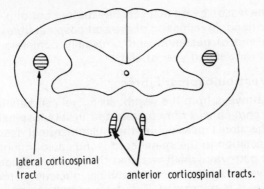

lateral corticospinal
tract

anterior corticospinal tracts.

Fig. 39. Transverse section of spinal cord to show position of corticospinal tracts.

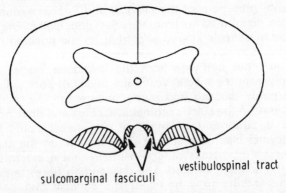

sulcomarginal fasciculi

vestibulospinal tract

Fig. 40. Transverse section of cervical spinal cord to show position of vestibulospinal fibres.

the lateral and anterior corticospinal tracts in a transverse section of the cervical region of the spinal cord.

It has been estimated that 55 per cent of all corticospinal fibres end in the cervical part of the spinal cord, 20 per cent in the thoracic part and 25 per cent in the lumbosacral part. Obviously, the pyramidal control over the upper limb is much greater than that over the lower limb the reason being that very fine motor control is needed for the hand. Myelination of the corticospinal fibres begins at the end of gestation and is usually complete by the end of the second year of life.

The Vestibulospinal Fibres

The pathways from the vestibular nuclei caudally into the spinal cord consist of two parts, the 'vestibulospinal tracts' and the fibres passing in the sulcomarginal fasciculus. Their position in the spinal cord is indicated in Figure 40.

The pathway which is called the 'vestibulospinal tract' is derived from the lateral vestibular nucleus of the same side, i.e. it is uncrossed. This tract is present throughout the length of the spinal cord and lies in the anterior white column. Most of the fibres of this tract terminate in the anterior grey horn of the cervical and lumbar expansions so are distributed to limb muscles principally. The tone of the muscles is altered according to the position of the head and in response to head movements.

The other pathway from the vestibular nuclei arises mainly from the medial vestibular nuclei of both sides, i.e. it is partly crossed and partly uncrossed. This pathway descends in the sulcomarginal fasciculus and does not extend throughout the length of the spinal cord. Some authorities claim that it only extends as far as the cervical spinal cord whereas others maintain that it extends into the thoracic spinal cord. The descending fibres terminate in the anterior grey horns of the cervical and perhaps thoracic regions and provide for change in the tone of the neck muscles as is needed to support the head in various positions. Rostrally, the fibres arising in the medial vestibular nucleus make up part of an important interconnecting bundle in the brain stem called the medial longitudinal fasciculus.

The Rubrospinal Tracts

The rubrospinal tracts originate in the red nuclei which lie in the midbrain. The fibres decussate in the midbrain and descend to take up a position in the spinal cord ventral to the lateral corticospinal tracts (Fig. 41). These fibres are sometimes claimed to be rudimentary in man but clear evidence for this is lacking although so far they have only been traced as far as the cervical and upper thoracic regions of the spinal cord. It is likely that many of the rubrospinal fibres in man are difficult to identify because they are thin and poorly myelinated. There are connections from the red nucleus to the reticular formation and thence to the spinal cord via the reticulospinal tracts, see below, and these connections may be more important in man than the rubrospinal tracts themselves.

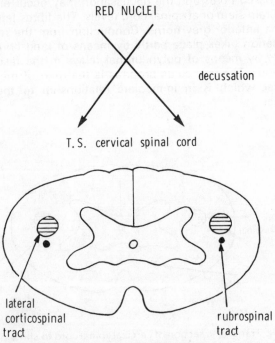

RED NUCLEI

decussation

T.S. cervical spinal cord

lateral corticospinal tract

rubrospinal tract

Fig. 41. The rubrospinal tracts.

The Reticulospinal Tracts

The reticular formation of the brain stem consists of neurons in areas not occupied by nuclei or tracts. It is difficult to organise these cells into definite groups. This diffuse arrangement is present in primitive vertebrates and has persisted in the mammalian brain where it makes an important contribution to many aspects of brain function as it has connections with all levels of the neuraxis.

Two groups of reticulospinal fibres are present in the spinal cord (Fig. 42). The anterior tract descends in the anterior white column as far as the lower cervical region and the lateral tract descends in the lateral white column as far as the thoracic region. Each tract has crossed and uncrossed fibres and the decussation may occur either in the brain stem or at spinal cord levels. The fibres terminate in the anterior grey horns. Conduction from the reticular formation takes place partly by means of long fibres and partly by means of polyneuronal relays in the fasciculus proprius. The fasciculus proprius is that part of the white matter which is in immediate relationship to the grey matter.

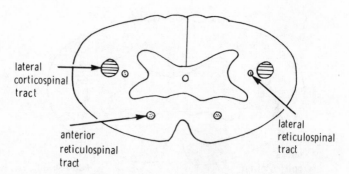

lateral corticospinal tract

anterior reticulospinal tract

lateral reticulospinal tract

Fig. 42. Transverse section of cervical spinal cord to show position of reticulospinal tracts.

The Tectospinal Tracts

The tectospinal tracts were not shown in the general scheme. They arise in the superior colliculi of the midbrain which are the reflex centres for vision. The fibres decussate in the midbrain and send information to the brain stem and spinal cord to bring about reflex postural movements in response to visual and perhaps auditory stimuli. Most of the fibres terminate in the anterior grey horns of the upper four cervical segments but a few reach the lower cervical spinal segments.

CHAPTER VIII

THE MEDULLA OBLONGATA, PONS AND FOURTH VENTRICLE

The Medulla Oblongata (Bulb)

The medulla oblongata is the direct and expanded upward continuation of the spinal cord and it consists of closed and open parts. The floor of the fourth ventricle (rhomboid fossa) occupies the posterior surface of the open part of the medulla oblongata and also extends rostrally to assume the same relationship to most of the pons.

The caudalmost part of the medulla oblongata resembles the spinal cord in many ways but the corticospinal tracts instead of occupying the lateral white columns, as they do in the spinal cord, lie on the ventral aspect of the medulla where they form two elevations, one on either side of the midline, called the pyramids (see Fig. 14). In the caudal part of the medulla oblongata 80 to 90 per cent of the corticospinal fibres cross to the lateral white column of the opposite side of the spinal cord. The anterior grey horn becomes separated from the central grey by the decussating corticospinal fibres which are travelling posteriorly and laterally to reach the lateral white column of the opposite side. Thus the continuity between the central grey matter and the anterior grey column, present throughout the spinal cord, is disrupted. The detached anterior grey column diminishes in size as it ascends; it supplies efferent fibres to the first cervical spinal nerve and the upper part of the spinal part of the accessory nerve. The change in position of the fibres constituting the pyramids is called the decussation of the pyramids and the crossing tracts may be seen in the depths of the anterior median fissure.

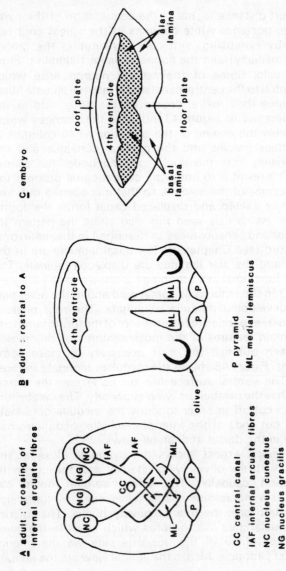

Fig. 43 Medulla oblongata: formation of fourth ventricle.

A adult : crossing of internal arcuate fibres

B adult : rostral to A

C embryo

CC central canal
IAF internal arcuate fibres
NC nucleus cuneatus
NG nucleus gracilis

P pyramid
ML medial lemniscus

A short distance rostral to the decussation of the pyramids the posterior white columns of the spinal cord terminate by synapsing with cells constituting the gracile nuclei (medially) and the cuneate nuclei (laterally). From these nuclei fibres of the second neuron arise which pass ventral to the central canal as the internal arcuate fibres to continue their rostral course on the other side as the medial lemniscus. Figure 43 indicates the changes which accompany the ending of the posterior white columns at the nucleus gracilis and the nucleus cuneatus and the fibres arising from the nuclei passing under the central canal. The result is to bring the central canal up onto the dorsal surface of the medulla so that it is opened out, and the widely dilated and displaced canal forms the fourth ventricle. As can be seen this also alters the pattern for the motor and sensory areas as described in the embryonic spinal cord (see Chapter II). The basal laminae are in the midline and the alar laminae are displaced laterally. The order of functional cell groupings is shown in the diagram (Fig. 44) in the embryonic spinal cord and in the open part of the developing medulla oblongata. The roof plate is enormously expanded to form the roof of the fourth ventricle.

The main features of the gross anatomy of this region have been outlined but it is necessary to make some additions. Figure 45 shows the medulla oblongata in three views. The ventral surface lies on bone and the dorsal surface has the cerebellum lying superiorly. The cerebellum has been cut off in order to show the medulla oblongata and the cut ends of the inferior cerebellar peduncles can be seen in the dorsal and lateral views.

The ventral aspect shows the pyramids close to the midline, with the olives lying laterally and the pyramidal decussation caudally. The olives contain nerve cell bodies in a horseshoe shape when seen in transverse section and form the inferior olivary nuclei. The inferior olivary nuclei give rise to fibres which cross to the cerebellar hemisphere of the opposite side via the inferior cerebellar peduncle. Also in the ventral view are the arcuate

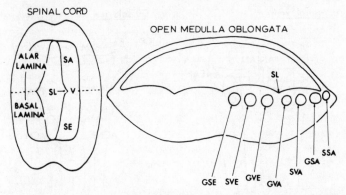

Fig. 44. Functional arrangement of cell columns in the embryo. SL=sulcus limitans; SA=somatic afferent cells; V=visceral cells; SE=somatic efferent cells; SSA=special somatic afferent; GSA= general somatic afferent; SVA=special visceral afferent; GVA= general visceral afferent; GVE=general visceral efferent; SVE= special visceral efferent; GSE=general somatic efferent.

nuclei which lie ventral to the pyramids. These nuclei give rise to fibres which, in effect, are aberrant pontocerebellar fibres. It is as if some of the nerve cells of the pons had slipped caudally. Two sets of fibres pass from the arcuate nuclei:

1. Fibres passing ventrolaterally over the ventral aspect of the medulla oblongata and over the olive to go to the inferior cerebellar peduncle. The anterior external arcuate fibres.

2. Fibres passing medially at first, then through the substance of the medulla oblongata in the midline to emerge on the floor of the fourth ventricle. They then pass laterally to the inferior cerebellar peduncle as the striae medullares of the fourth ventricle. This band of fibres demarcates the fourth ventricle into a caudal part associated with the medulla oblongata and a rostral part associated with the pons.

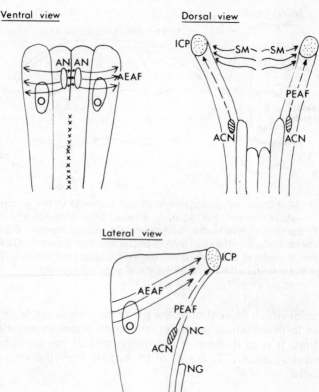

Fig. 45. Medulla oblongata. O=olive; AN=arcuate nucleus; AEAF=anterior external arcuate fibres→ICP; ICP=inferior cerebellar peduncle; ACN=accessory cuneate nucleus; SM=striae medullares of fourth ventricle; PEAF=posterior external arcuate fibres→ICP; NC=nucleus cuneatus; NG=nucleus gracilis.

The dorsal aspect of the medulla oblongata shows the gracile tubercles and the cuneate tubercles, the caudal part of the floor of the fourth ventricle and the inferior cerebellar peduncles. The striae medullares have been described already as aberrant pontocerebellar fibres. The major component of the inferior cerebellar peduncles are the posterior spinocerebellar tracts which will be discussed with the cerebellum. Lateral to the cuneate tubercle, under which lies the cuneate nucleus, is the lateral or accessory cuneate nucleus which gives rise to the posterior external arcuate fibres. These fibres are concerned with the transmission of proprioceptive information to the cerebellum from the first four cervical nerves.

Some of the white matter of the medulla oblongata has been mentioned, that is, corticospinal fibres, medial lemnisci, posterior spinocerebellar tracts and external arcuate fibres. In addition there are deeply placed tracts, well-defined nuclei of certain cranial nerves and the reticular formation.

The Pons

That part of the brain stem lying rostral to the medulla oblongata is the pons. It is characterised by thick bundles of fibres running transversely across its ventral aspect and turning dorsally into the cerebellum as the middle cerebellar peduncles. In transverse section (Fig. 46), the pons has an open, caudal part and a closed, rostral part. The pons is divisible into two regions dorsoventrally:

1. The dorsal part or tegmentum which is hidden by the cerebellum in the intact specimen and is similar to the medulla oblongata and midbrain in that it contains ascending and descending tracts and nuclei of cranial nerves. The dorsal surface of the tegmental part of the pons is contributing to the formation of the floor of the fourth ventricle.

2. The ventral or basilar part which is the convex mass of transversely running fibres seen in a ventral view of the brain. These transversely running fibres do not encircle the pons, they arise from grey matter within it called the pontine nuclei. The fibres from the pontine nuclei cross to the other side and converge posteriorly to form the middle cere-

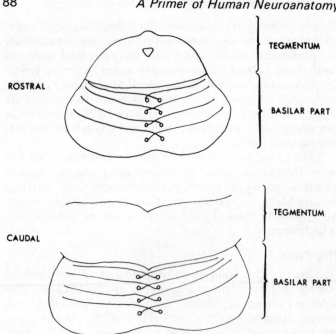

Fig. 46. Transverse sections of the pons.

bellar peduncles where the fifth cranial nerves emerge through the substance of the pons. The fifth nerves are used to demarcate the pons, lying medial to them, from the middle cerebellar peduncles, lying lateral to them. Fibres from the cerebral cortex terminate on the pontine nuclei of the same side and axons of the latter cells make up the contralateral middle cerebellar peduncle. The basilar part of the pons is a relay station providing a connection from the cerebral cortex of one side to the cerebellar hemisphere of the other side as part of a circuit to improve the efficiency of voluntary movements. The basilar part of the pons receives the crura cerebri at its rostral margin and emits the pyramids at its caudal margin. The corticospinal tracts have to traverse the transversely running pontine fibres of the basilar part of the pons at right angles. As the corticospinal tracts pass through the basilar part of the pons they are split up into small bundles.

The Fourth Ventricle

The fourth ventricle is a diamond-shaped cavity the floor of which is called the rhomboid fossa. It lies behind the upper or open part of the medulla oblongata and behind most of the pons. The fourth ventricle lies in front of the cerebellum and it has two lateral angles where the inferior cerebellar peduncles meet the pons. At these lateral angles there are extensions of the fourth ventricle called the lateral recesses which are made of ependyma and which extend laterally over the posterior aspect of the inferior cerebellar peduncles on each side to open into the pontine cistern via the lateral apertures of Luschka.

The tent-shaped roof of the fourth ventricle protrudes into the cerebellum. Figure 47 shows the general plan of the roof with the cerebellum removed.

The roof can be divided into three parts rostrocaudally:
1. The rostral part of the roof is formed on either side by the converging superior cerebellar peduncles and the V-shaped gap between them is bridged by the superior medullary velum;
2. The inferior medullary velum is a thin, incomplete sheet of tissue attached to the cerebellum rostrally and continuous caudally with the ependymal part of the roof of the fourth ventricle;
3. The most caudal part of the roof is ventricular ependyma in which there is a deficiency called the median aperture or the foramen of Magendie which opens into the cerebellomedullary cistern.

The choroid plexus of the fourth ventricle is suspended from the roof and is T-shaped. The extremities of the bar of the 'T' wind round the inferior cerebellar peduncles, thus lying in the lateral recesses and often protruding at

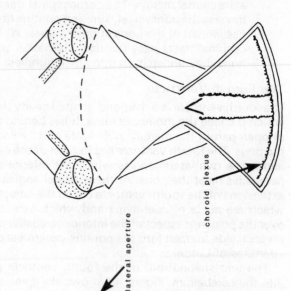

Roof cut along dashed line and reflected caudally to expose the choroid plexus on its deep surface.

choroid plexus

lateral aperture

Roof intact

lateral recess

median aperture

Fig. 47. The roof of the fourth ventricle.

the ends of the lateral recesses through the foramina of Luschka.

The floor of the fourth ventricle is broad in its midportion and narrows rostrally and caudally (Fig. 48). The floor is divided into symmetrical halves by a median groove with an eminence on each side of the groove. Each half is further subdivided into medial and lateral areas by the sulcus limitans. The part associated with the medulla oblongata is demarcated from the part behind the pons by a band of fibres, the striae medullares of the fourth ventricle. The rostral part of the floor shows two circular elevations called the facial colliculi and indicates where the fibres of the facial nerves loop round the nuclei of the abducent nerves. At the rostral end of the sulcus limitans the floor of the fourth ventricle appears blue due to the presence of pigmented cells. This area is the locus coeruleus.

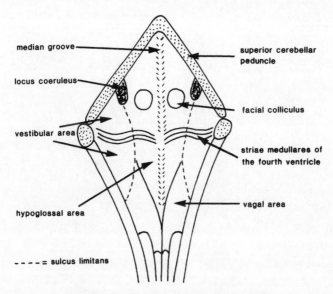

median groove

superior cerebellar peduncle

locus coeruleus

facial colliculus

vestibular area

striae medullares of the fourth ventricle

vagal area

hypoglossal area

- - - - = sulcus limitans

Fig. 48. The floor of the fourth ventricle.

The part of the floor lying lateral to the sulcus limitans is the vestibular area as most of the vestibular nuclear complex lies beneath it. In the part of the floor lying medial to the sulcus limitans and caudal to the striae medullares there are two main areas, the hypoglossal triangle and the vagal triangle.

CHAPTER IX

THE CEREBELLUM

Introduction and Development

The cerebellum is essentially a motor part of the brain and it functions in the maintenance of equilibrium and in the co-ordination of muscle action. It is especially important in the synchronisation of muscles which make up a functional group. This synchronisation is necessary in voluntary movements although the cerebellum does not initiate voluntary movements. Damage to the cerebellum shows as disorders of motor functions in the absence of paralysis. Man has maximal development of the cerebellum as he has precise, motor movements.

The cerebellum lies posterior to the medulla oblongata, pons and fourth ventricle and occupies the greater part of the posterior cranial fossa. The cerebellum develops from a ridge of tissue in the thin roof of the fourth ventricle, opposite the pontine part of the brain stem (Fig. 49). The expansion to form the cerebellum shows the nodule and the posterolateral fissure at an early stage. Then the fissura prima develops which effectively divides the anterior lobe from the middle lobe. The middle lobe shows the greatest amount of expansion and forms the major part of the adult cerebellum.

Although the developing cerebellum enlarges posteriorly because of the development of the middle lobe it does not greatly increase its attachment to the brain stem. This differential growth of the middle lobe between the anterior lobe and the posterior lobe causes the superior and inferior cerebellar penduncles to hinge at their attachments carrying with them the superior and inferior medullary vela which are

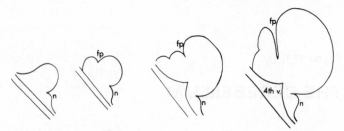

Fig. 49. Development of the cerebellum. n=nodule; fp=fissura prima; 4th v.=fourth ventricle.

attached to their medial borders and which form the main part of the roof of the fourth ventricle. This results in a tent-like elevation of the roof into the anterior surface of the cerebellum.

General Topography

The cerebellum has two hemispheres and a median part which is called the vermis. The whole structure has upper and lower surfaces separated by the horizontal fissure and it also possesses a circumferential margin. The surface of the cerebellum shows characteristic closely set transverse and rather curved sulci separated by narrow gyri.

Figure 50 shows the surfaces of the cerebellum. The superior vermis is present as an undivided ridge of tissue but the inferior vermis is divided into the uvula and pyramid in the midline and a tonsil on each side. The nodule of the posterior lobe has developed lateral extensions called the flocculi. The fissura prima demarcates the anterior lobe from the middle lobe and the posterolateral fissure demarcates the middle lobe from the posterior lobe.

The cerebellum may be divided in a physiological way according to its connections. The archicerebellum is the posterior or flocculonodular lobe, it has connections with the balancing system. The paleocerebellum consists of the anterior lobe together with the pyramid and uvula and it receives proprioceptive and tactile information. The neo-cerebellum consists of the middle lobe except the pyramid

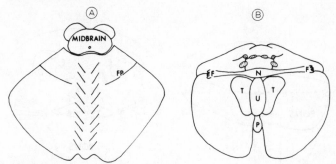

Fig. 50. The surfaces of the cerebellum. A. Superior surface; B. Inferior surface. FP=fissura prima; F=flocculus; N=nodule; T=tonsil; U=uvula; P=pyramid.

and uvula and it has been developed in conjunction with the cerebral cortex.

The cerebellar cortex has a uniform structure throughout, unlike the cerebral cortex, and consists of grey matter covering narrow leaflike laminae projecting from the central white matter. The ridges of cortex are called the cerebellar folia. There are four collections of nerve-cell bodies on each side forming the deep grey matter of the cerebellum. Figure 51 shows a side view of the cerebellum together with a horizontal section to demonstrate the cerebellar nuclei. The largest nucleus is the dentate and, moving medially, there is the emboliform nucleus and the globose nucleus (the two latter nuclei forming the nucleus interpositus of some lower animals) and situated most medially is the fastigial nucleus.

The Spinocerebellar Tracts

Cerebellar function is based primarily on the receipt of information from the body via the spinocerebellar tracts as to the position of the body parts. There are two groups of nerve-cell fibres forming the posterior and anterior spino-cerebellar tracts which lie in the lateral white columns of the spinal cord. Figure 52 indicates the position of the posterior and anterior spinocerebellar tracts.

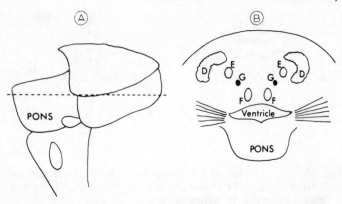

Fig. 51. The cerebellum. A. Lateral view; B. Horizontal section. D=dentate nucleus; E=emboliform nucleus; G=globose nucleus; F=fastigial nucleus.

The posterior spinocerebellar tracts are composed of nerve-cell fibres which are mostly from the same side. The nerve-cell bodies of the second neuron are lying in the thoracic nucleus area of the posterior horn of grey matter of the spinal cord from the eighth cervical segment to the third or fourth lumbar spinal segment. Cells receive col-

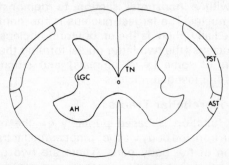

Fig. 52. Transverse section of thoracic spinal cord. TN= thoracic nucleus; PST=posterior spinocerebellar tract; AST= anterior spinocerebellar tract; LGC=lateral grey column; AH= anterior horn.

laterals from the posterior columns which are carrying the sensations of proprioception and discriminatory touch. The posterior spinocerebellar tracts pass rostrally and form the major component of the inferior cerebellar peduncles (see later).

The anterior spinocerebellar tracts are made up of axons from both sides of the spinal cord whose origin has not been finally decided. Some authorities think that the cell bodies lie in the anterior grey horn but in the lower lumbar and sacral regions there seems to be a column of cells which may be analogous to the thoracic nucleus. The anterior spinocerebellar tracts pass rostrally as far as the midbrain and then turn caudally to reach the cerebellum via the superior cerebellar peduncles (see later). This tract is sometimes called the indirect tract.

The Cerebellar Peduncles

There are three pairs of cerebellar peduncles connecting the cerebellum to other parts of the central nervous system:

1. The superior cerebellar peduncles (brachia conjunctiva) connecting the cerebellum to the midbrain;
2. The middle cerebellar peduncles (brachia pontis) connecting the cerebellum to the pons;
3. The inferior cerebellar peduncles (restiform bodies) which connect the cerebellum to the medulla oblongata.

The superior cerebellar peduncles form the lateral walls of the rostral part of the fourth ventricle. The efferent fibres of the superior cerebellar peduncles pass medially and decussate at the level of the inferior colliculi of the midbrain and then pass to the red nuclei at the level of the superior colliculi of the midbrain. A few fibres terminate on the red nuclei but most fibres form a capsule around the red nuclei and then continue rostrally to the thalami. The efferent component of the superior cerebellar peduncles consists of fibres from the dentate, emboliform and globose nuclei of the cerebellum. The afferent components are the anterior spinocerebellar tracts, which have travelled into the midbrain and then doubled back to reach the superior cerebellar peduncles, and fibres from one of the pairs of nuclei of the fifth cranial nerve, the mesencephalic nuclei.

The middle cerebellar peduncles are the largest of the three pairs of peduncles. They are formed from fibres which arise from the pontine nuclei in the opposite half of the basilar part of the pons. These pontine nuclei receive information from the cerebral cortex. The fibres of the middle cerebellar peduncles terminate in the neocerebellum. There are no efferent fibres in the middle cerebellar peduncles, all the fibres are afferent pontocerebellar fibres.

The inferior cerebellar peduncles form on the postero-lateral surface of the medulla oblongata. The composition of these peduncles is complex:

1. Efferent fibres:
    (a) Fastigiobulbar fibres from both sides travelling to the vestibular nuclei and the reticular formation;
    (b) Cerebellocortico-vestibular fibres from the flocculonodular lobe (the archicerebellum);
2. Afferent fibres:
    (a) The posterior spinocerebellar tracts;
    (b) Olivocerebellar fibres from the inferior olivary nucleus of the opposite side;
    (c) Fibres from the vestibular nuclei;
    (d) Fibres from the reticular formation;
    (e) Fibres from the accessory cuneate nuclei;
    (f) Fibres from the arcuate nuclei (aberrant ponto-cerebellar fibres).

The Cerebellar Cortex

The cerebellum receives a great variety of sensory information which is monitored or co-ordinated in the cortex. The upper part of Fig. 53 shows a diagram of the cerebellar cortex, which has two layers: an outer molecular layer with Purkinje cells lying in its deepest part and an inner granular cell layer containing both granule and Golgi cells. The Purkinje cells are characteristic of the cerebellum and are flattened in a direction transverse to the long axis of a folium.

The dendrites of the Purkinje cells extend into the molecular layer where they branch profusely always in the transverse plane of the cerebellar folium. In sections cut parallel to the long axis of a cerebellar folium the cell and the dendritic branching is seen in profile and is limited to a narrow area. The Purkinje cells receive climbing fibres, the granule cells receive mossy fibres. The basket cells receive information from granule cells and give off collaterals which ensheath Purkinje cells. There is a layer of superficial basket cells called stellate cells which receive information from granule cells. Each of the fourteen million Purkinje cells is said to have one million synapses.

The afferent fibres are of two types already mentioned, that is mossy fibres and climbing fibres. The circuitry is organised in the following way: both these afferent fibres enter the cerebellum and give collaterals to the cerebellar nuclei, they then terminate in the cortex. The climbing fibres terminate on Purkinje cells and the mossy fibres terminate on granule cells which subsequently synapse with Purkinje, basket and stellate cells. The granule cell axons pass towards the outer layers of the cortex and divide into two branches which run parallel to the long axis of the cerebellar folia. The Purkinje cells provide the output from the cerebellar cortex by means of their axons which travel to the cerebellar nuclei. The axonic processes of cells of the cerebellar nuclei form the efferent fibres from the cerebellum. In addition, fibres arise directly from the flocculonodular lobe without passing through the nuclei and form efferent fibres in the inferior cerebellar peduncles going to the vestibular nuclei.

The above description has omitted any explanation of the role of the Golgi cells. The mossy fibres terminate on granule cells (see above) and the ends of the fibres are expanded to form a structure called a mossy fibre rosette. Associated with the rosette are dendrites of granule cells and axons of Golgi cells and this synaptic complex is called a cerebellar glomerulus (lower part of Fig. 53). The dendritic branches of the Golgi cells extend throughout the cerebellar cortex but are most extensive in the outer part of the molecular layer

Section cut in a plane transverse to the long
axis of a cerebellar folium

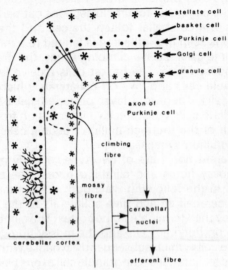

→ stellate cell
→ basket cell
→ Purkinje cell
→ Golgi cell
→ granule cell

axon of
Purkinje cell

climbing
fibre

mossy
fibre

cerebellar
nuclei

cerebellar cortex

efferent fibre

Enlargement of the area within dashed line
(Cerebellar glomerulus)

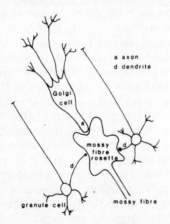

a axon
d dendrite

Golgi
cell

mossy
fibre
rosette

granule cell   mossy fibre

Fig. 53. The cerebellar cortex.

where they come into contact with the axons of the granule cells which run parallel to the long axis of the cerebellar folia. In the glomerulus the mossy fibre/granule cell synapse is considered to be excitatory whereas the Golgi cell/mossy fibre synapse is inhibitory. As the main input to the Golgi cell is derived from the parallel fibres of the granule cells the Golgi cell is functioning as a negative feedback to the mossy fibre/granule cell relay.

The cerebellum appears to function as a monitor and modulator of muscle movement. Recent evidence suggests that the cerebellum organises information from various sources and then participates in the control of motor function by transmission to the brain stem nuclei and the thalamic nuclei which in turn can modify the response of cortical regions associated with motor function.

Every part of the cerebellar cortex receives directly or indirectly, inputs from two sources, that is, the mossy fibres and the climbing fibres. these mossy and climbing fibres are carrying essentially 'sensory' data. The output from the Purkinje cell axons is inhibitory and it is exerted on the cerebellar nuclei but the output of the cerebellar nuclei is excitatory so the nuclei must receive an excitatory input but the means by which this is achieved is not known. The cerebellar cortex transforms all input into inhibition so there cannot be reverberating chains of neurons in the cerebellar cortex and this means that the cerebellum can provide a clear and quick response to any particular input but there is no possibility of dynamic storage of information by impulses circulating in complex neuronal pathways.

CHAPTER X

THE MIDBRAIN

General Topography

The midbrain is a short, thick stalk which connects the pons to the cerebral hemispheres. In the adult is is not more than 2.0 cm long and about 2.5 cm in width. The ventral surface extends from the pons to the mamillary bodies of the diencephalon. The midbrain is traversed by the cerebral aqueduct which connects the third ventricle rostrally with the fourth ventricle caudally. The cerebral aqueduct is surrounded by the central grey substance which includes the nuclei of the third and fourth cranial nerves and the mesencephalic nuclei of the fifth cranial nerves.

Figure 54 shows the midbrain in a lateral view. The midbrain is divisible into two parts, a small posterior part called the tectum which lies dorsal to the cerebral aqueduct and a large anterior part called the cerebral peduncles which lies ventral to the cerebral aqueduct. Winding round the lateral aspect of the midbrain are the trochlear nerves, the only cranial nerves with a dorsal attachment. The trochlear nerves emerge inferior to the inferior colliculi.

The tectum shows four rounded elevations called the corpora quadrigemina. The two superior elevations are the superior colliculi and the two inferior ones are the inferior colliculi. The superior colliculi are concerned with reflex pathways for vision and have bands of fibres going to them from the lateral geniculate bodies of the thalamus which are the superior brachia. The superior colliculi are connected to cranial nerve nuclei and the spinal cord by means of the tectobulbar and tectospinal tracts. The pretectal region lies immediately rostral to the superior colliculi at

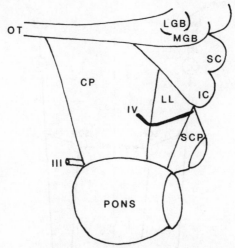

Fig. 54. Side view of midbrain. OT=optic tract; MGB=medial geniculate body; LGB=lateral geniculate body; CP=cerebral peduncle; LL=lateral lemniscus; SC superior colliculus; IC=inferior colliculus; SCP=superior cerebellar peduncle; III=third nerve; IV=fourth nerve.

the level of the posterior commissure. It is considered to be the principal midbrain centre involved in the pupillary light reflex (see Chapter XVIII).

The inferior colliculi are on the direct pathway for hearing. Fibres ascend from the cochlear nuclei to the inferior colliculi and then pass via the lateral lemnisci which are sometimes visible in the gross specimen as separate bands of fibres lying superficial to the superior cerebellar peduncles. Fibres proceed via the brachia of the inferior colliculi to the medial geniculate bodies of the thalami.

The Pathway for Hearing

There is a basic difference between the superior and inferior colliculi, the former being reflex centres for sight whereas the latter are on the direct pathway for hearing. Figure 55

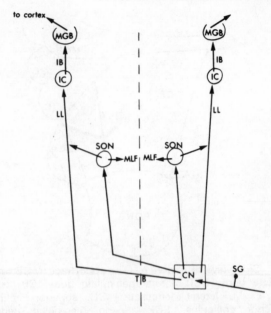

Fig. 55. The pathway for hearing. MGB=medial geniculate body; IB=inferior brachium; IC=inferior colliculus; LL=lateral lemniscus; SON=superior olivary nucleus; MLF=medial longitudinal fasciculus; TB=trapezoid body; CN=cochlear nuclei; SG=spiral ganglion.

shows diagrammatically the pathway for hearing. Impulses from the hearing apparatus (the organ of Corti in the cochlea) pass to the spiral ganglion in the cochlea. The central branches of the ganglion cells go to the cochlear nuclei in the medulla oblongata where they can take one of three courses:

1. To the inferior colliculus of the same side. (This pathway is not acknowledged by all authorities);
2. To the inferior colliculus of the other side, crossing in the tegmentum of the pons as the trapezoid body;
3. To the superior olivary nucleus of either side from

which a second neuron sends processes to the medial longitudinal fasciculus of its own side or to the lateral lemniscus of its own side.

Fibres which are ascending to the inferior colliculus via the lateral lemniscus then proceed to the medial geniculate body of the thalamus via the inferior brachium. Then fibres go to the part of the cortex concerned with hearing which is situated in the temporal lobe. It seems to require four neurons to transmit hearing impulses whereas for ordinary sensation only three are usually needed. Also, each ear is represented bilaterally in the cortex. This means that total destruction of the auditory cortex of one side will result in partial hearing loss in both ears.

The Cerebral Peduncles

The cerebral peduncles are the larger, anterior portion of the midbrain and they are divided into three parts ventrodorsally (Fig. 56):

1. The crura cerebri or basis pedunculi;
2. The substantia nigra;
3. The tegmentum.

The crura cerebri are rope-like structures composed of fibres arising in the cerebral cortex of each hemisphere and converging onto the inferior surfaces of the hemispheres to emerge as the crura cerebri where the optic tracts cross their lateral surfaces. The nerve fibres in the crura cerebri arise from all parts of the hemispheres and form cortico-pontine (to pons), corticobulbar (to the nuclei of the cranial nerves), and corticospinal (to the spinal cord) groups of nerve fibres.

The substantia nigra consists of large nerve cells with black pigment in their cytoplasm. They connect the tegmentum with the corpus striatum of the ipselateral hemisphere. The substantia nigra extends rostrally into the hypothalamus and it functions as a part of the extra-pyramidal system.

The tegmentum is a mixture of grey and white matter and

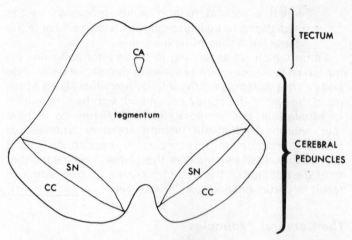

Fig. 56. Transverse section of midbrain. CA=cerebral aqueduct;
SN=substantia nigra; CC=crus cerebri.

it is continuous caudally with the tegmental part of the pons.
Rostrally it is continuous with the hypothalamus and
posteriorly it is continuous with the tectum in the region
of the cerebral aqueduct.

CHAPTER XI

THE CRANIAL NERVE NUCLEI AND THE TRACTS OF THE BRAIN STEM

Introduction

The principal nuclei and fibre tracts in the brain stem will be described. Long-fibre tracts will be traced in the medulla oblongata, pons and midbrain and the larger nuclei of the cranial nerves will be identified in the brain stem. As well as clearly defined nuclei and tracts there are other areas, difficult to organise into groups, which comprise the reticular formation.

The Cranial Nerve Nuclei in the Brain Stem

Figure 57 shows the cranial nerve nuclei projected onto an outline of the posterior aspect of the brain stem with the cerebellum removed. The sensory nuclei are indicated on the right-hand side and the motor nuclei are indicated on the left-hand side. In fact, both types of nuclei are present on both sides.

The third, fourth and sixth nerves (Figs. 57, 61, 62) are the three cranial nerves which supply the extraocular muscles with motor fibres.

The oculomotor nerve—The oculomotor nucleus includes a parasympathetic component called the Edinger-Westphal nucleus which lies dorsal to the rostral two-thirds of the main oculomotor nucleus. The nucleus lies at the level of the superior colliculus in the ventral part of the periaqueductal grey matter of the midbrain. Oculomotor fibres are partly crossed and partly uncrossed.

The trochlear nerve—The nucleus of the trochlear nerve

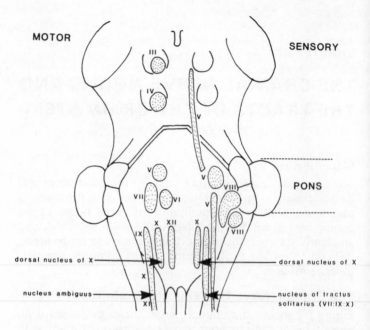

MOTOR

SENSORY

PONS

dorsal nucleus of X

dorsal nucleus of X

nucleus ambiguus

nucleus of tractus
solitarius (VII:IX:X)

Fig. 57. Cranial nerve nuclei.

supplies the superior oblique muscle only and is caudal
to the oculomotor nucleus at the level of the inferior
colliculus in the ventral part of the periaqueductal grey
matter (Figs. 57, 62). The nerve fibres have an unusual
course and this is the only nerve to emerge dorsally from
the brain stem. Small bundles of fibres wind round the
periaqueductal grey matter, decussate in the superior
medullary velum and emerge inferior to the inferior
colliculus.

The abducent nerve—The abducent nerve (Figs. 57, 61),
supplying motor fibres to the lateral rectus muscle, has its
nucleus beneath the facial colliculus of the rhomboid
fossa. A bundle of facial nerve fibres courses over the

nucleus and so forms the elevation known as the facial colliculus of the floor of the fourth ventricle (Fig. 58).

The trigeminal nerve—The trigeminal nerve has a motor and a sensory component. The sensory component embodies three nuclei:

1. The mesencephalic nucleus;
2. The chief sensory nucleus in the pons;
3. The lower sensory nucleus in the medulla oblongata.

Most of the cell bodies of the primary sensory neurons of the fifth nerve are in the trigeminal (semilunar) ganglion which lies outside the central nervous system but some of the primary sensory neurons lie in the mesencephalic nucleus. The mesencephalic nucleus is concerned with proprioceptive sensation, particularly from the muscles of mastication, and most of the peripheral processes of these neurons lie in the mandibular division of the trigeminal nerve. The main sensory nucleus in the pons is concerned with touch from the major part of the face and scalp, and this nucleus is mainly associated with agreeable sensations. The lower sensory nucleus of the spinal tract of the fifth nerve conducts impulses for pain and temperature. This nucleus can usefully be thought of as an ascending part of the substantia gelatinosa of the spinal cord (see Chapter VI). Owing to the wide distribution of these sensory nuclei in the

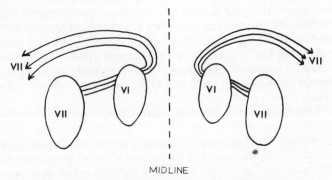

MIDLINE

Fig. 58. Loop of facial nerve fibres round abducent nucleus.

brain stem some of the incoming fibres of the trigeminal nerve turn rostrally and others caudally into the medulla oblongata where they lie on the surface of the lower sensory nucleus. The latter constitutes the spinal tract of the fifth nerve. The lower sensory nucleus of the fifth nerve is concerned with disagreeable sensations.

Efferent fibres from the sensory trigeminal nuclei proceed to the sensory areas of the cerebral hemispheres via the thalami but also have connections to motor nuclei in the brain stem in order to initiate reflexes. Fibres from the sensory nuclei are distributed to the reticular formation to bring about 'activation' via the reticular activating system.

The motor nucleus of the fifth nerve, supplying motor fibres to the muscles of mastication, lies in the pons medial to the main sensory nucleus.

The facial nerve—The facial nerve has sensory and motor components (Figs. 57, 60, 61). The sensory and parasympathetic fibres of the seventh nerve together constitute the 'nervus intermedius'. The sensory component of the facial nerve has two parts, one supplying taste buds and the other contributing cutaneous fibres to the external ear. The cell bodies of the primary sensory neurons of the seventh nerve lie in the geniculate ganglion which is situated on a bend on the nerve deep within the petrous temporal bone of the skull. The sensory nucleus is the rostral end of a column of cells called the nucleus of the tractus solitarius which also contains cell bodies of the ninth and tenth cranial nerves. Most of the nucleus of the tractus solitarius is associated with taste. The cutaneous sensory component enters the brain stem via the nervus intermedius but joins the spinal tract of the fifth nerve.

The facial nerve has two motor components, one for the facial muscles of expression and one for the sub-mandibular and sublingual salivary glands and the lacrimal gland. The motor nucleus of the facial nerve is situated in the pons and the fibres run medially round the abducent nucleus and then over the rostral end of that nucleus

(Fig. 58). The superior salivatory and lacrimal nuclei are medial to the motor nucleus of the facial nerve. These nuclei provide parasympathetic fibres which leave the brain stem in the nervus intermedius and then follow devious routes to their final destinations. The superior salivatory nucleus and the lacrimal nucleus come under the control of the hypothalamus by means of a tract called the dorsal longitudinal fasciculus.

The vestibulocochlear nerve—The vestibulocochlear nuclei lie in the medulla oblongata and the pons (Figs. 57, 60, 61). The cochlear nuclei, for hearing, have a dorsal and ventral part on each side and lie on the dorsal and ventrolateral aspects of the inferior cerebellar peduncle. The vestibular nuclei, for balance, are made up of four groups of cells on each side, that is, superior, inferior, lateral and medial. The medial nucleus extends from the medulla oblongata at the level of the rostral part of the olive into the caudal region of the pons. The inferior and lateral nuclei lie between the medial nucleus and the inferior cerebellar peduncle, the lateral nucleus extending rostrally as far as the pontomedullary junction. The rostral extremity of the lateral nucleus becomes continuous with the superior nucleus which lies in the pons.

The glossopharyngeal, vagus and accessory nerves—The glossopharyngeal, vagus and accessory nerves have to be thought of as an entity as they have many functions in common and share certain nuclei in the medulla oblongata (Figs. 57, 60). The glossopharyngeal and vagus nerves include fibres for the special visceral sense of taste which are relayed in the nucleus of the tractus solitarius, the first order neurons lying in ganglia outside the central nervous system. There are also sensory fibres for pain, temperature and touch but the central connections of these fibres are uncertain. The cell bodies of afferent neurons for general visceral reflexes are also in the ganglia of the ninth and tenth nerves, that is, baroreceptors in the carotid sinus and aortic arch. The central processes of these neurons end in the most caudal part of the nucleus of the tractus solitarius and from this site connections are made with the motor nucleus of the vagus nerve and with the hypothalamus. There is another view of the position of the cell bodies on which general visceral afferents terminate and that is that they lie in the sensory part of the dorsal nucleus of the vagus.

The ninth, tenth and eleventh cranial nerves all include motor fibres for the supply of striated muscles and the ninth and tenth nerves also contain parasympathetic efferents. The nucleus ambiguus is a column of typical motor neurons labelled IX, X and XI in Figure 57. This nucleus supplies muscles of the soft palate, pharynx and larynx and the striated muscle of the upper part of the oesophagus, the striated muscles derived from branchial arches. The sternocleidomastoid and the trapezius are supplied by the spinal root of the accessory nerve. The cranial root of the accessory nerve joins the vagus, that is, it is accessory to the vagus. The main parasympathetic nucleus is the dorsal motor nucleus of the vagus whence fibres will be supplied to the thorax and abdomen. The superior extremity of the dorsal motor nucleus of the vagus is called the inferior salivatory nucleus and fibres from this nucleus are included in the ninth nerve to supply the parotid gland eventually.

The hypoglossal nerve—The hypoglossal nucleus lies between the dorsal nucleus of the vagus and the midline of the medulla oblongata (Figs. 57, 60). From the hypoglossal nucleus motor fibres are supplied to the intrinsic muscles of the tongue and three of the extrinsic muscles of the tongue. The nucleus receives afferents from the nucleus of the tractus solitarius and from the sensory trigeminal nuclei for reflex movements of the tongue in swallowing, chewing and sucking.

The nuclei in the medulla oblongata should now be related to the functional arrangement of cell columns as described in Chapter VIII. Figure 59 shows the arrangement in the developing medulla oblongata and in the adult. Starting laterally, the special somatic afferent cells are present in the nuclei of the vestibulocochlear nerve. General somatic afferent cells are associated with the spinal nucleus of the fifth nerve. Special visceral afferent and general

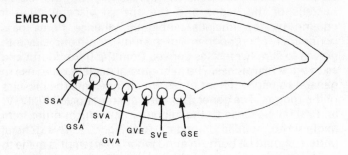

EMBRYO

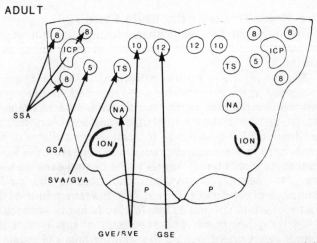

ADULT

Fig. 59. Functional arrangement of cell columns in the medulla oblongata. TS=tractus and nucleus solitarius; NA=nucleus ambiguus; P=pyramid; ION=inferior olivary nucleus; ICP= inferior cerebellar peduncle; SSA=special somatic afferent; GSA= general somatic afferent; SVA=special visceral afferent; GVA= general visceral afferent; GVE=general visceral efferent; SVE= special visceral efferent; GSE=general somatic efferent.

visceral afferent cells are found together in the nucleus of the tractus solitarius and are concerned with taste and general visceral afferent sensation. The general visceral efferent column of cells is represented by the dorsal nucleus of the vagus and the special visceral efferent column by the nucleus ambiguus whence fibres pass peripherally as components of the ninth, tenth and eleventh nerves to supply muscles derived from the third, fourth and sixth branchial arches. The hypoglossal nucleus gives rise to general somatic efferent fibres which innervate the muscles of the tongue. The general somatic efferent nuclei, III, IV, VI and XII, all lie close to the midline in numerical order from midbrain to medulla oblongata (see Fig. 57). This general pattern should be borne in mind when an attempt is made to memorise the position of the cranial nerve nuclei.

The Major Tracts of the Brain Stem

The tracts of the brain stem are bilateral but in the following account they are described in the singular, as is customary.

1. **Tracts in the medulla oblongata**—Major changes take place at the junction between the medulla oblongata and the spinal cord. Firstly, the pyramidal decussation at the caudal part of the medulla oblongata and secondly, the termination of the posterior (dorsal) white column of the spinal cord in the nucleus gracilis and cuneatus; the fibres from these nuclei travel ventral to the central canal to form the great sensory decussation and become the medial lemniscus of the other side (Fig. 43). the termination of the posterior white column as stated results in the absence of fibres lying posteriorly and the result of this is that the central canal opens out so that the medulla oblongata is described as having a caudal, closed part and a rostral, open part. The open part of the medualla oblongata forms the caudal part of the floor of the fourth ventricle.

Figure 60 shows transverse sections of the upper (open) and lower (closed) parts of the medulla oblongata. In the lower medulla oblongata the spinal tract and nucleus of

the fifth nerve lie laterally. The fibres of the great sensory
decussation form the medial lemniscus. The anterior and
lateral spinothalamic tracts are separate and lateral to the
medial lemniscus. The pyramidal fibres lie ventrally. The
upper medulla oblongata shows the nuclei of the eighth
nerve lying disposed around the inferior cerebellar peduncle
(see earlier) with the spinal nucleus of the fifth nerve lying
medial to the latter structure. Close to the midline and lying

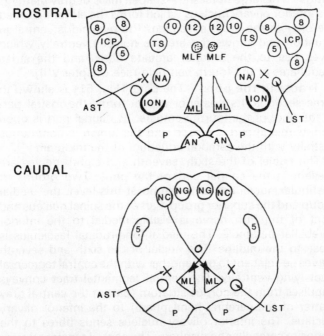

Fig. 60. Medulla oblongata (sections). ICP=inferior cerebellar
peduncle; MLF=medial longitudinal fasciculus; TS=tractus and
nucleus solitarius; NA=nucleus ambiguus; ML=medial lemniscus; ION=inferior olivary nucleus; P=pyramid; AN=arcuate
nucleus; ADT=anterior spinothalamic tract; LST=lateral spinothalamic tract; NG=nucleus gracilis; NC=nucleus cuneatus.

just under the floor of the fourth ventricle is the hypoglossal nucleus. Ventral to the nucleus of the twelfth nerve is the medial longitudinal fasciculus which is an intersegmental tract connecting the vestibular nuclei with other brain stem nuclei, in particular the nuclei of the third, fourth and sixth cranial nerves. Also seen are the dorsal nucleus of the vagus, the nucleus of the tractus solitarius and the nucleus ambiguus. The medial lemniscus lies close to the midline and the anterior and lateral spinothalamic tracts are still separate entities. The large horseshoe-shaped mass of grey matter is the inferior olivary nucleus which forms the elevation called the olive in the gross specimen. The pyramid is ventral in situation and shows the arcuate nucleus ventrally which gives rise to the anterior arcuate fibres and the striae medullares of the fourth ventricle (see Chapter VIII).

2. Tracts in the pons—The pons (Fig. 61) is shown in three sections. Its posterior aspect forms the rostral part of the floor of the fourth ventricle. Its caudal part is open and its rostral part is closed and the lumen is continuous rostrally with the cerebral aqueduct of the midbrain.

The nuclei of the sixth, seventh and eighth nerves are present in the caudal part of the pons. Two groups of vestibular nuclei are to be found at this level, the medial group and the superior group. Part of the spinal nucleus and tract of the fifth nerve is visible medial to the inferior cerebellar peduncle. The medial longitudinal fasciculus is close to the midline. The nuclei of the sixth and seventh nerves lie adjacent to one another with the central tegmental tract lying ventrally. The central tegmental tract conveys impulses from the corpus striatum (part of the central grey matter of the cerebral hemisphere) to the inferior olivary nucleus. The inferior olivary nucleus sends fibres to the opposite cerebellar hemisphere. The central tegmental tract also carries ascending impulses from the reticular formation to the thalamus.

The medial lemniscus is changing in position from being paramedian, as in the upper medulla oblongata, to being transversely placed. Close to the lateral border of the medial

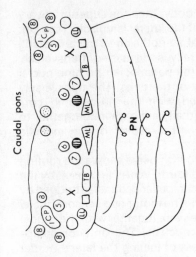

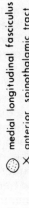

Caudal pons

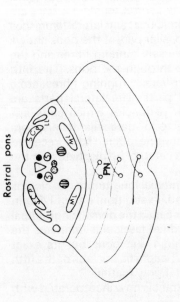

Rostral pons

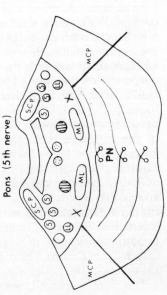

Pons (5th nerve)

Fig. 61. The pons. SCP=superior cerebellar peduncle; MCP=middle cerebellar peduncle; ML=medial lemniscus; LL=lateral lemniscus; PN=pontine nuclei; TB=trapezoid body; ICP=inferior cerebellar peduncle.

⊙ medial longitudinal fasciculus
✕ anterior spinothalamic tract
◯ lateral spinothalamic tract
⊜ central tegmental tract
● dorsal longitudinal fasciculus
□ superior olivary nucleus

lemniscus lies the trapezoid body, then the superior olivary nucleus and the beginning of the lateral lemniscus (see Fig. 55). The anterior and lateral spinothalamic tracts are still separate entities. Lying ventrally is the mass of transversely running fibres arising from the paramedian pontine nuclei and forming the basilar part of the pons. The transversely running fibres are interlaced with the descending corticospinal fibres which eventually are gathered together to form the pyramid on the ventral aspect of the medulla oblongata.

The pons at the level of the fifth nerve shows the roofing over of the rostral part of the fourth ventricle caused by the convergence of the superior cerebellar peduncles bridged by the superior medullary velum. The motor and sensory nuclei of the trigeminal nerve can be seen, together with the caudal part of the mesencephalic nucleus. The anterior spinothalamic tract is in the process of joining the lateral border of the now transversely placed medial lemniscus. The medial longitudinal fasciculus and the central tegmental tract are evident. The lateral spinothalamic tract and lateral lemniscus are close to each other. The basilar part of the pons shows the pontine nuclei, the transversely running fibres and the emergence of the fifth nerve through the pons. The fifth nerves divide the mass of transversely running fibres into a medial part and two lateral parts. The lateral parts are forming the middle cerebellar peduncles which carry impulses from the pontine nuclei to the cerebellar hemisphere of the opposite side. The pontine nuclei have received corticopontine fibres from the cerebral hemispheres via the cerebral peduncles.

The rostral pons shows the medial longitudinal fasciculus and central tegmental tract and, in addition, a tract lying in the periaqueductal grey matter called the dorsal longitudinal fasciculus. The dorsal longitudinal fasciculus connects the hypothalamus with the midbrain and pons but its exact extent is not known. The mesencephalic nucleus of the fifth nerve lies in the periaqueductal grey matter.

The anterior spinothalamic tract is now incorporated with

the medial lemniscus and the lateral spinothalamic tract lies laterally. The lateral lemniscus is taking up a position on the surface of the superior cerebellar peduncle where it can sometimes be recognised in the intact specimen.

3. Tracts in the midbrain — Figure 62 shows the midbrain at two levels. At the level of the inferior colliculus in the region of the cerebral aqueduct can be seen the dorsal longitudinal fasciculus, the mesencephalic nucleus of the fifth nerve and the nucleus of the fourth nerve. Ventral to the central grey matter lies the medial longitudinal fasciculus. The central position in the tegmentum is occupied by the decussation of the superior cerebellar peduncles. The central tegmental tract and the medial lemniscus are lateral to the decussation of the superior cerebellar peduncles. The lateral lemniscus can be seen terminating in the inferior colliculus. Ventrally lies the substantia nigra and the crus cerebri.

At the level of the superior colliculus the periaqueductal grey matter has the dorsal longitudinal fasciculus, the mesencephalic nucleus of the fifth nerve and the nucleus of the third nerve lying within it. Ventral to the periaqueductal grey matter is the medial longitudinal fasciculus. The major feature of this section is the presence of the red nucleus surrounded by a capsule of fibres from the superior cerebellar peduncle. Dorsolateral to the red nucleus lie the central tegmental tract and the medial lemniscus. There are two midline decussations at this level: (1) the dorsal tegmental decussation which is the crossing of the tecto-spinal tracts and (2) The ventral tegmental decussation which is where the rubrospinal and rubroreticular fibres cross to the other side.

The medial and lateral geniculate bodies or nuclei of the thalamus are usually evident in a section through the midbrain at this level although they are not part of the mid-brain. The medial geniculate nucleus is concerned with hearing and the lateral geniculate nucleus is concerned with vision.

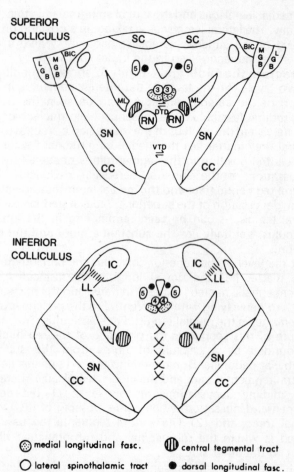

Fig. 62. The midbrain. DTD=dorsal tegmental decussation; SC=
superior colliculus; LGB=lateral geniculate body; MGB=medial
geniculate body; BIC=brachium of inf. colliculus; RN=red
nucleus; VTD=ventral tegmental decussation; ML=medial lemniscus; IC=inferior colliculus; LL=lateral lemniscus; CC=crus
cerebri; SN=substantia nigra.

The Parasympathetic Supply to the Salivary Glands

It is now possible to review the parasympathetic supply to the salivary glands. The superior salivatory nucleus lies medial to the motor nucleus of the facial nerve and it supplies fibres to the submandibular and sublingual salivary glands. The preganglionic fibres pass through the nervus intermedius and the chorda tympani branch of the facial nerve and reach the submandibular ganglion by way of a branch of the fifth nerve. Postganglionic fibres then arise from the ganglion and pass to the submandibular and sublingual salivary glands.

The inferior salivatory nucleus is the rostral end of the dorsal nucleus of the vagus. The preganglionic fibres reach the otic ganglion via the glossopharyngeal nerve and then pass to the parotid gland via the trigeminal nerve.

The Special Sense of Taste

The receptors for taste are taste buds present in the tongue, soft palate and epiglottis. The anterior two-thirds of the tongue is supplied by sensory fibres from the facial nerve (see above). The taste fibres arise from unipolar cells in the geniculate ganglion of the facial nerve and the peripheral processes reach the tongue by way of the chorda tympani nerve. The central processes travel to the nucleus of the tractus solitarius.

The posterior third of the tongue is supplied by the peripheral processes of ganglion cells in the inferior ganglion of the glossopharyngeal nerve. The central processes travel to the nucleus of the tractus solitarius.

The epiglottis taste fibres have their cell bodies in the inferior ganglion of the vagus nerve and the central processes of the ganglion cells go to the nucleus of the tractus solitarius. The pathway from the nucleus of the tractus solitarius to the thalamus is thought to be incorporated into the contralateral medial lemniscus.

CHAPTER XII

THE THIRD VENTRICLE

General Position

The third ventricle is a narrow cavity lying in the midline between the right and left thalami and is continuous inferiorly with the cerebral aqueduct. The lateral ventricles communicate with the third ventricle via the interventricular foramina and each foramen lies behind the fornix and in front of the anterior tubercle of the thalamus. The floor is formed by the hypothalamus and the subthalamus. A double layer of pia mater is above the third ventricle lying in the forward extension of the transverse fissue which is a horizontal slit situated below the caudal end of the corpus callosum. Figure 63 shows a median sagittal section through the brain demonstrating the extent and boundaries of the third ventricle.

The Floor

The floor of the third ventricle extends from the rostral end of the cerebral aqueduct, above the mamillary bodies and tuber cinereum, into the infundibular recess and then over the optic chiasma into the optic recess.

The Anterior Wall

The anterior wall consists of the lamina terminalis and, superiorly, the anterior commissure.

The Roof

The roof of the third ventricle is made of ependyma which is invaginated on each side of the midline by pia mater. The pia mater has been introduced into this position via the traverse fissure. The pia mater and ependyma together make up the linear choroid plexus of the third ventricle. The roof extends from the interventricular foramina rostrally to the habenular commissure caudally and a diverticulum projects over the latter to form the suprapineal recess.

The Posterior Wall

The posterior wall extends from the habenular commissure superiorly to the cerebral aqueduct inferiorly. The pineal body possesses a pineal recess and the posterior commissure lies inferior to it.

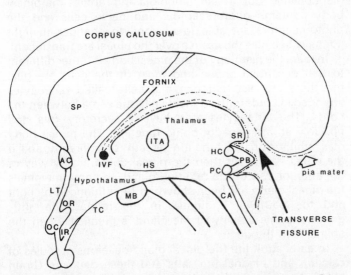

Fig. 63. Median sagittal section of brain; third ventricle. CA= cerebral aqueduct; IVF=interventricular foramen; MB=mamillary body; TC=tuber cinereum; IR=infundibular recess; OC=optic chiasma; OR=optic recess; LT=lamina terminalis; AC=anterior commissure; HC=habenular commissure; SR=suprapineal recess; PB=pineal body; PC=posterior commissure; HS=hypothalamic sulcus; ITA=interthalamic adhesion; SP=septum pellucidum.

The Lateral Wall

The lateral wall of the third ventricle consists of the anterior two-thirds of the thalamus and the hypothalamus. The demarcation between the thalamus and hypothalamus is indicated by the hypothalamic sulcus. In approximately 80 per cent of human brains an adhesion is present between the thalami called the interthalamic adhesion which is considered by most authorities to have no functional significance.

The Pineal Body (Epiphysis)

The pineal body is a projection of tissue from the dorsal diencephalic roof. In fish, amphibia and reptiles the pineal body contains photoreceptors and nerve cells and the photoreceptors are able to respond to changes in light intensity because the tissues over the pineal are translucent.

In man, the histology of the pineal body is rather different to that described above and most of the cells are glial but there are also parenchymal cells called pineocytes arranged in cords with connective tissue septa between the cords. The pineocytes may have a secretory role and possibly an antigonadotrophic function. The pineal body may inhibit gonadal function directly or indirectly and if the effect is indirect then the pineal could act by way of the anterior part of the pituitary gland. In some mammals the pineal gland has been shown to be influenced by light and the pathway originates in the retina. The antigonadotrophic activity of the gland is greatest when the animal is in the dark.

In early adult life the pineal gland develops granules of calcium and magnesium salts and these deposits (brain sand) can frequently be seen in an X-ray photograph of the skull and so can be useful in demonstrating that the pineal gland has moved to one side of the median plane as a result of a space-occupying condition on the opposite side which has distorted the brain.

CHAPTER XIII

THE CEREBRAL HEMISPHERES

General

The cerebral hemispheres consist of grey and white matter. Some of the grey matter is deeply situated and some lies on the surface forming the cortex of the cerebral hemispheres. The cortex is convoluted, with elevations (gyri) and depressions (sulci), a general description will be found in Chapter III, Figures 17, 18 and 19.

Functional Areas of the Cerebral Cortex

The cerebral cortex has sulci and gyri and some of these are known to have functional significance. On the superolateral surface the sulci of importance are the lateral sulcus, the central sulcus and the calcarine sulcus (Fig. 64). The motor area is rostral to the central sulcus and is called the precentral gyrus; in this area the cortex is unusually thick and contains the giant pyramidal cells of Betz. In addition, there is a secondary motor area which abuts onto the lateral sulcus. Also present on the superolateral surface is the motor-speech area (usually in the left hemisphere) lying between the horizontal and ascending rami of the lateral sulcus. It is concerned with the control of movements of the larynx and tongue. The auditory area is on the superolateral surface and is the cortical area to which auditory impulses are primarily relayed. The auditory area lies on the middle of the superior surface of the superior temporal gyrus within the lateral sulcus and to a small extent on the lateral surface of that gyrus, inferior to the postcentral gyrus.

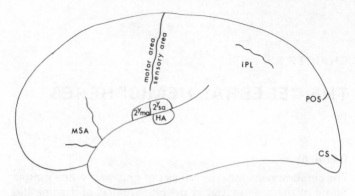

Fig. 64. Functional areas of cerebral cortex; superolateral surface.
MSA=motor speech area; 2^{y}ma=secondary motor area; 2^{y}sa=
secondary sensory area; HA=hearing (auditory) area; IPL=
inferior parietal lobule; POS=parieto-occipital sulcus; CS=
calcarine sulcus.

The inferior parietal lobule is the area associated with the
recognition of symbols and may differ in function in the two
hemispheres. Lying caudal to the central sulcus is the
sensory area in the postcentral gyrus and inferior to this in
the postcentral gyrus is the secondary sensory area. The way
in which the body is represented in the main motor and
sensory areas has been described in Chapters VI and VII,
Figures 35 and 37.

The medial surface of the cerebral hemisphere has the
central sulcus encroaching onto it (Fig. 65). There is a
supplementary motor area lying just inferior and rostral to
the principal leg and foot area. Here the body is represented
lying horizontally with the head directed rostrally. The
threshold for stimulation of the supplementary motor area
in man is higher than that of the precentral region. Evidence
indicates that the supplementary motor area functions bilaterally. The paracentral lobule is on the medial surface
and it is the area of cortex concerned with sphincter control
(see Fig. 18). The calcarine sulcus divides the medial
surface of the occipital lobe into the cuneus, lying between

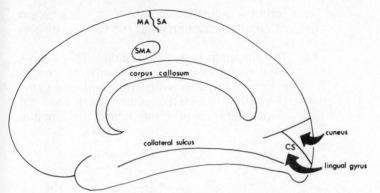

Fig. 65. Functional areas of cerebral cortex; medial surface. MA= motor area; SMA=supplementary motor area; SA=sensory area; CS=calcarine sulcus (vision).

it and the parieto-occipital sulcus, and the lingual gyrus which lies between the calcarine and the collateral sulci (see Fig. 19). The cortex on both sides of the calcarine sulcus is where the nerve fibres carrying visual impulses to the cortex end. The visual cortex can be recognised with the unaided eye because a white stria runs through it parallel to the surface, this area is sometimes called the striate cortex.

The White Matter of the Cerebral Hemispheres

The fibres comprising the white matter are divided into three systems on the basis of their courses and connections:

1. Projection fibres which connect the cerebral cortex and the deep grey of the hemispheres with the thalamus, the nuclei of the brain stem and the spinal cord;

2. Association fibres which connect one part of a hemisphere with another part of the same hemisphere. They vary enormously in length. Short association fibres may pass from one part of a gyrus to another part of the same gyrus or they may

loop round a sulcus to terminate in an adjacent gyrus. Certain association fibres run for long distances (Fig. 66):

(a)   The cingulum (meaning a girdle). This bundle is so called because it surrounds the corpus callosum together with the cingulate gyrus (Fig. 18) in which it is embedded. It links the medial surface of the frontal lobe to the temporal lobe;

Medial view   Superolateral view

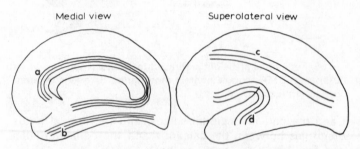

Fig. 66. Association fibres of the cerebral hemispheres. a= cingulum; b=inferior longitudinal bundle; c=superior longitudinal bundle; d=fasciculus uncinatus.

(b)   The inferior longitudinal bundle. This group of fibres passes from the occipital lobe to the temporal lobe;

(c)   The superior longitudinal bundle. This group of fibres passes from the frontal lobe to the occipital lobe;

(d)   Fasciculus uncinatus. This bundle connects the temporal lobe with the frontal lobe;

3.   Commissural fibres. Commissural fibres cross the midline to connect the two hemispheres:

(a)   The corpus callosum. The corpus callosum is the great commissure connecting the two hemispheres. In median section (Fig. 67) it is seen to have an inferiorly placed rostrum which is attached to the lamina terminalis (already

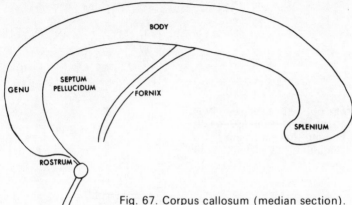

Fig. 67. Corpus callosum (median section).

seen in the third ventricle), then there is a bend called the genu, then the body or trunk and, finally, a posterior expanded splenium. The fornix is attached to the corpus callosum by the septum pellucidum.

The corpus callosum unites the medial surfaces of the cerebral hemispheres for nearly half of their rostrocaudal length and lies nearer the rostral than the caudal ends of the hemispheres. The upper surface of the corpus callosum forms the floor of the middle part of the longitudinal fissure. The anterior cerebral vessels lie on the pia mater covering the superior surface of the corpus callosum. The corpus callosum, viewed from above (Fig. 68), shows the forceps minor arching rostrally from the genu and the forceps major arching caudally from the splenium. The tapetum is a special layer of fibres of the corpus callosum which pass through the splenium and then turn inferiorly to reach the temporal lobe and the inferior part of the occipital lobe. These fibres making up the tapetum are unusual in that they

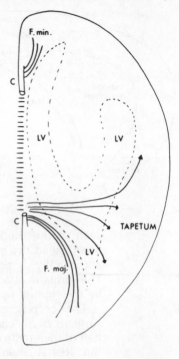

Fig. 68. Corpus callosum from above. F.maj.=forceps major; F. min.=forceps minor; C=cingulum; LV=lateral ventricle.

do not interlace with the fibres of the internal capsule (see Chapter XIX), because they lie above the retrolentiform and sublentiform fibres of the optic and auditory radiations and posterior to the main fibres of the internal capsule. The tapetum is closely associated with parts of the lateral ventricles.

In the midline the corpus callosum overlies the roof of the third ventricle but is separated from it by the tela choroidea of the third ventricle. The sheet of pia mater extends anteriorly between the splenium of the corpus callosum and the dorsal surface of the midbrain and the pineal body. It contains the posterior choroidal branches of the posterior cerebral arteries and the internal cerebral veins. The internal cerebral veins drain into the great cerebral vein inferior to the splenium;

(b) The anterior commissure. The anterior commissure lies in the superior part of the lamina terminalis. Its fibres connect the temporal lobes;

(c) The optic chiasma. The optic chiasma will be considered when the visual pathway is discussed in Chapter XVIII;

(d) The posterior commissure. The posterior commissure lies dorsal to the upper part of the cerebral aqueduct and inferior to the root of the pineal body. It is composed of fibres arising mainly in the midbrain;

(e) The habenular commissure. This commissure lies superior to the pineal recess and is associated with a region called the habenular triangle which is where the habenular nuclei lie.

The Development of the Cerebral Hemispheres

The third ventricle is the cavity of the forebrain. Each lateral ventricle is the result of the lateral outgrowth of the telencephalon on each side. Because of the mode of development described below the lateral ventricles and the structures within the forebrain form C-shaped hemispirals.

The forebrain grows in a semi-helical fashion, starting from a transverse axis running though the interventricular foramina (Fig. 69). The original cortex is the insula and it becomes covered by newer cortex. The inferior part of the insula is the limen insulae and it is continuous with the later cortex but the remainder of the insula is cut off from the later cortex by the circular sulcus. The pieces of cortex covering the insula are called opercula (=lids) and there are three opercula, the frontal, the parietal and the temporal.

Because the cerebral hemispheres grow in this way the cavities within them (lateral ventricles) are in the main

C-shaped, the 'C' being formed by the central part and the inferior horn of each ventricle and there are the additional diverticula of the anterior and posterior horns. The central part and inferior horn can be considered to be mirror images of each other, that is, structures present in the roof of the central part will be found in the floor of the inferior horn and the converse is also true.

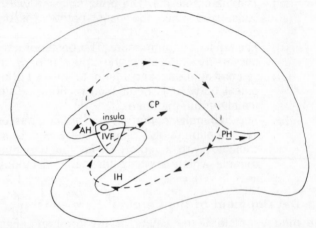

Fig. 69. Direction of growth of cerebral hemispheres and lateral ventricles.

IVF = interventricular foramen

→ = direction of growth of cerebral hemispheres

AH = anterior horn
CP = central part
PH = posterior horn
IH = inferior horn
} of lateral ventricle

The Functions of the Cerebral Hemispheres

The brain of man is distinguished by the enormous size of the cerebral cortex and the evolution of the cortex is related to the development of extremely elaborate behavioural patterns. Computers are being used in an effort to establish the circuitry of the mammalian cortex but there are probably 5 million cells beneath each square centimetre of surface cortex so the problem of mapping connections between the cells remains a mammoth task.

There is one striking feature of the brain of man which may be unique among mammals. This unique feature is the phenomenon of cerebral dominance. In some higher functions, which are believed to be cortical, one hemisphere appears to be the more important and so is called the dominant hemisphere for that function. The capacity for speech in adult man is usually controlled by the left hemisphere and recent as well as classical work has indicated an anatomical basis for this finding. It has been discovered that in 65 per cent of brains the planum temporale, an area of the upper surface of the superior temporal gyrus, is larger on the left than on the right. The planum temporale is a large part of Wernicke's area which is cerebral cortex associated with the auditory area and functions in the general comprehension of language. The left hemisphere is dominant with respect to speech and the right hemisphere is more concerned with symbol recognition and spatial integration. In effect, what is happening is that the two hemispheres work in different ways from the same information and that the two hemispheres working together may give greater power to the brain.

Involved with the known facts of cerebral dominance is manual preference or 'handedness'. The relationship of cerebral dominance to handedness seems less clear than was assumed in the past. However, it can be stated that in right-handed individuals it is nearly always the left hemisphere which is dominant for speech and therefore governs language. In left-handed individuals the dominant hemisphere for speech may be the right or the left.

If the two hemispheres have rather differing functions but act together then there must be exchange of information from one hemisphere to the other. The corpus callosum is the largest of the commissures connecting the two hemispheres and is incomplete at birth but is almost complete by the second or third year of life. It is believed that before completion of the corpus callosum both hemispheres may be able to handle linguistic data. It has been noticed that left-hemisphere lesions in young children do not cause total loss of speech so that the right hemisphere must be capable of developing language skills. Much research has been performed to investigate the functions of the corpus callosum by using animals in which the corpus callosum has been sectioned.

The so-called 'higher cortical functions' involve complex correlations and the use of previous reactions to the same or similar events together with discrimination of sensory impulses. This is called 'associative memory'. Impulses which enter the primary sensory area of the brain produce sensations which are clearly defined but not of a nature that would enable recognition of an object. In order to recognise an object, areas around the primary sensory areas are required, and they combine sensation into a pattern which may be recalled. In the region of the inferior parietal lobule the patterns of sensation are more complex so that tactile and movement impulses can be built up into stereognosis. Any object is represented by a set of memories built up from several sensory sources which are dependent on previous experience. When the sensory sources form the same set as the previous experience then the object is recognised.

CHAPTER XIV

THE LATERAL VENTRICLES

General

Each lateral ventricle lies within a cerebral hemisphere and the anterior horn, central part and inferior horn together form a C-shaped hemispiral (Fig. 69) with the inferior horn lying lateral to the central part and anterior horn. The posterior horn is a backward-projecting diverticulum from the hemispiral. The cavity of the lateral ventricle is triangular in cross section with a roof, floor and medial wall. Owing to the hemispiral configuration the roof of the central part is continuous with the floor of the inferior horn and the roof of the inferior horn is continuous with the floor of the central part. There are structures associated with the lateral ventricles which also show the same C-shaped hemispiral arrangement.

The first of the aforementioned structures is the caudate nucleus which is one of the deep grey masses of the telencephalon (Fig. 70). The head of the caudate nucleus lies rostral to the thalamus while the body lies round its outer edge and the tail sweeps inferiorly and laterally into the inferior horn. The head and body of the caudate nucleus lie in the floor of the anterior horn of the lateral ventricle and the tail lies in the roof of its inferior horn. The amygdaloid body lies anterior to the tail of the caudate nucleus.

The second C-shaped structure related to the lateral ventricle is the hippocampus and its rostral continuation which is the fornix. The hippocampus lies in the floor of the inferior horn of the lateral ventricle. The fornix continues forwards over the superior aspect of the thalamus

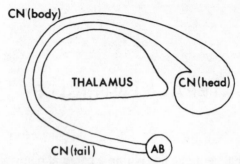

Fig. 70. Structures around the lateral ventricle—I. CN=caudate nucleus; AB=amygdaloid body.

but lies medial to the body of the caudate nucleus and not above it (Fig. 71). The hippocampus is inrolled cortex and it is continuous with the uncus anteriorly; the uncus is an area of cortex seen on the inferior surface of the cerebral hemispheres (Fig. 19). The hippocampus is cortex but it does not appear grey because it is covered by a layer of white fibres called the alveus. The white fibres (alveus) pass medially to form a ridge, the fimbria, on the medial edge of the hippocampus. It is the fimbria which continues rostrally as the fornix, passes over the thalamus

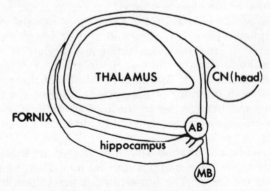

Fig. 71. Structures around the lateral ventricle—II. CN=caudate nucleus; AB=amygdaloid body; MB=mamillary body.

and then terminates in the mamillary body. Thus the hippocampus is in the floor of the inferior horn while its rostral continuation before it turns inferiorly to the mamillary body forms the medial wall of the central part of the lateral ventricle.

The third C-shaped structure associated with the lateral ventricle is the stria terminalis. This band of fibres passes from the amygdaloid body, along the roof of the inferior horn of the lateral ventricle and over the superior aspect of the thalamus to terminate in the grey matter present around the anterior commissure. As it passes over the thalamus it lies in the floor of the central part of the lateral ventricle.

The medial wall of the lateral ventricle is formed, like the roof of the third ventricle, by ependyma and is invaginated by pia mater to form the choroid plexus of the lateral ventricle. The line along which this has occurred is called the choroid fissure and it is C-shaped in form. The choroid fissure extends from the interventricular foramen to the anterior extremity of the inferior horn of the lateral ventricle. Figure 72 shows the position of the choroid fissure. The upper part lies between the thalamus and fornix, the middle part lies between thalamus and fornix and the lower part lies between the stria terminalis in the roof of the inferior horn and the fimbria of the hippocampus lying in the floor of the inferior horn. The upper part of the choroid plexus derives its pia mater from the lateral edge of the fold of pia mater which has passed into the transverse fissure inferior to the splenium of the corpus callosum. The lower part of the choroid plexus derives its pia mater from the inferior surface of the cerebral hemisphere and the lateral surface of the midbrain.

Arteries and Veins

The arterial supply of the lateral ventricles arises partly from the internal carotid arteries as the anterior choroidal arteries which enter the lateral ventricles at the anterior extremities of the inferior horns. Other arteries (posterior

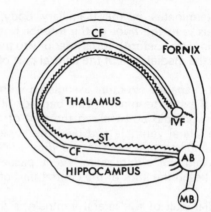

Fig. 72. The choroid fissure. CF=choroid fissure; IVF=interventricular foramen; ST=stria terminalis; AB=amygdaloid body; MB=mamillary body.

choroidal) arise from the posterior cerebral arteries and these pass into the transverse fissure (Fig. 63) to supply the choroid plexuses of the central part of the lateral ventricles.

The venous drainage of the choroid plexuses arises in the inferior horns of the lateral ventricles and passes through the interventricular foramina to join the thalamo-striate veins (Fig. 73). The thalamostriate vein runs with the stria terminalis over the superior aspect of the thalamus. The choroidal veins and thalamostriate veins join in the region of the interventricular foramina to give rise to the right and left internal cerebral veins. The right and left internal cerebral veins drain into the great cerebral vein.

The different parts of the lateral ventricles will now be discussed in some detail (Fig. 74).

The Anterior Horn

The anterior horn projects downwards and forwards into the frontal lobe. It is triangular in cross section. The greater part of the floor of the anterior horn is formed by the rounded head of the caudate nucleus with a small

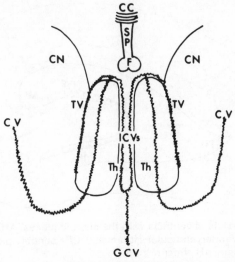

Fig. 73. The thalamus from above. CC=corpus callosum; SP= septum pellucidum; F=fornix; ICVs=internal cerebral veins; Th= thalamus; TV=thalamostriate vein; GCV=great cerebral vein; CV=choroidal vein; CN=caudate nucleus.

contribution from the rostrum of the corpus callosum, the anterior wall is formed by the posterior surface of the genu and the rostrum of the corpus callosum and the roof is limited by the trunk of the corpus callosum. The medial wall of the anterior horn is formed by the septum pellucidum, which also serves to separate it from its fellow of the opposite side. The septum pellucidum is a membranous structure with two layers which extends from the corpus callosum to the fornix. Sometimes a cavity develops between the two layers of the septum pellucidum which is termed the cavum pellucidum. There is no choroid plexus in the anterior horn.

The Central Part

The central part of the lateral ventricle is defined as extending from the interventricular foramen to the splenium of

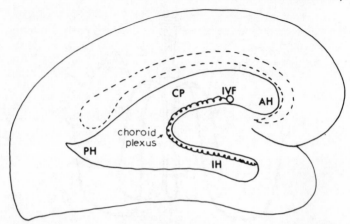

Fig. 74. The lateral ventricle with the choroid plexus. AH=anterior horn; IVF=interventricular foramen; CP=central part; PH= posterior horn; IH=inferior horn.

the corpus callosum (Fig. 75). The medial wall is composed of septum pellucidum with the fornix lying inferiorly. The roof and floor usually meet laterally. The floor is the most complicated part of the central part of the lateral ventricle and from medial to lateral side the following structures are present: choroid plexus with choroidal vein; thalamus; thalamostriate vein with stria terminalis and the caudate nucleus.

The Posterior Horn

The posterior horn begins at the splenium of the corpus callosum and·curves backwards and medially into the occipital lobe (Fig. 76). It is sometimes absent. The roof, lateral wall and floor of the posterior horn is formed by fibres of the tapetum of the corpus callosum. There is no choroid plexus in the posterior horn. The inferomedial wall shows two ridges:

1. The bulb of the posterior horn caused by forceps major of the corpus callosum;

2. The calcar avis which is due to the depth of the calcarine sulcus on the medial surface of the cerebral hemisphere.

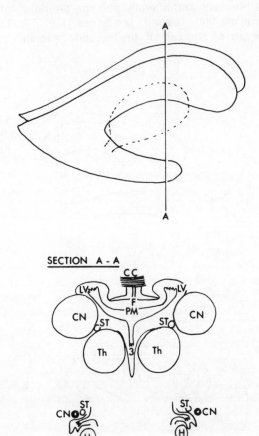

Fig. 75. Lateral ventricle; central part. CC=corpus callosum; F=fornix; PM=pia mater; 3=third ventricle; LV=lateral ventricle (central part); CN=caudate nucleus; ST=stria terminalis; Th= thalamus; H=hippocampus.

The Inferior Horn

The inferior horn of the lateral ventricle is the continuation of the ventricular cavity into the temporal lobe. The cavity extends forwards and laterally into the temporal lobe and then turns medially towards the uncus (Fig. 77). The roof is made up of the tail of the caudate nucleus and the

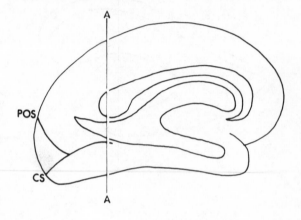

Section A-A

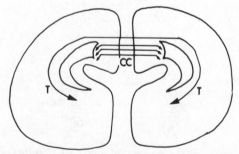

Fig. 76. Lateral ventricle; posterior horn. POS=parieto-occipital sulcus; CS=calcarine sulcus; CC=corpus callosum (splenium); T=tapetum.

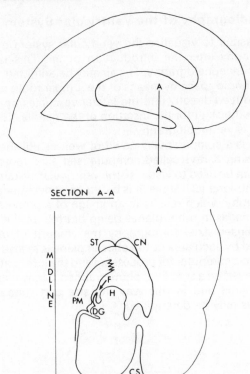

SECTION A-A

Fig. 77. Lateral ventricle; inferior horn. PM=pia mater; F=fimbria; H=hippocampus; DG=dentate gyrus; CN=caudate nucleus; CS=collateral sulcus; ST=stria terminalis.

stria terminalis which becomes continuous with the amygdaloid body at the tip of the inferior horn. The lateral wall is made up of the tapetum of the corpus callosum. The medial wall is deficient and is made of ependyma which has been pushed into the cavity by pia mater to form the choroid plexus of the inferior horn. The floor is broad posteriorly and may show an elevation called the collateral eminence due to the depth of infolding of the collateral sulcus.

The Radiography of the Ventricular System

It is possible to visualise the ventricular system by X-ray photography after the introduction of air. This is called pneumoencephalography. The air may be admitted into the subarachnoid space by means of the lumbar route or it may be introduced directly into the lateral ventricles by making a hole in the skull for the insertion of the needle. The latter method is ventriculography.

There is a comparatively new but well-established technique using X-rays called computerised axial tomography which can be used to visualise the ventricular system and to detect intracranial lesions. It is based on conventional X-ray tomography which results in an image of a predetermined plane, images in other planes being blurred. In the case of computerised axial tomography the amount of radiation absorbed by each area of the chosen plane is measured and passed to a computer for processing and the information can be displayed on a screen or photographed. Many planes can be examined and in this way the size and shape of the ventricles may be determined.

CHAPTER XV

THE OLFACTORY PATHWAYS AND THE LIMBIC SYSTEM

General

The olfactory pathways and the limbic system are closely associated with one another anatomically and represent the oldest part of the forebrain. The rhinencephalon refers to the olfactory part of the brain and the use of this term at the present state of knowledge is fraught with difficulties. Some authorities refer to the rhinencephalon and then divide it into an olfactory and a limbic part, others keep the term rhinencephalon for the olfactory part of the brain and regard the limbic system as a separate entity. More terminological problems arise because some workers describe a limbic *lobe* which is composed of the olfactory pathways and the limbic system together. During the evolution of mammals the area of the brain concerned with smell regressed but portions of the original olfactory part of the brain developed and acquired functions other than smell. In the following discussion the use of the term rhinencephalon will be avoided and the olfactory pathways and limbic system will be considered separately. Because the olfactory pathways and the limbic system are the oldest part of the forebrain they have been disturbed by growth of subsequent structures; this partly accounts for their complexity (Fig. 78).

The Olfactory Pathways

The olfactory nerves whose cell bodies lie in the olfactory epithelium pass from the upper part of the nasal cavity, through the cribriform plate of the ethmoid bone of the skull into the olfactory bulb which lies superior to the cribriform plate on the inferior surface of the frontal lobe (Fig. 19). The olfactory bulb possesses three types of cells, mitral, granular and tufted, and the dendrites of the mitral and tufted cells receive olfactory impulses from the olfactory nerves. The granular cells probably function as internuncial

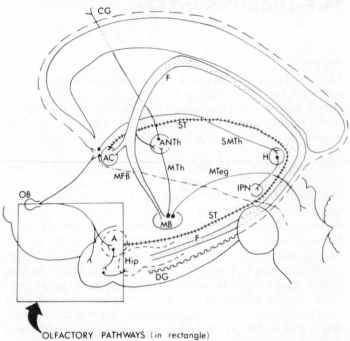

OLFACTORY PATHWAYS (in rectangle)

Fig. 78. The olfactory pathways and the limbic system. OB = olfactory bulb; AC = anterior commissure; ANTh = anterior nucleus of thalamus; H = habenular nucleus; A = amygdaloid nucleus; Hip = hippocampus; MB = mamillary body; IPN = interpeduncular nucleus; F = fornix; MTh = mamillothalamic tract; MTeg = mamillotegmental tract; DG = dentate gyrus; CG = cingulate gyrus; ST = stria terminalis; SMTh = stria medullaris thalami; MFB = medial forebrain bundle.

neurons. The axons of the mitral and tufted cells form the olfactory tract on each side which splits into the medial and lateral olfactory striae. The medial olfactory stria terminates in the medial olfactory (septal) area close to the anterior commissure. It is doubtful if the septal area makes an important contribution to the sense of smell at the conscious level; it should be included in the limbic system (see later). The lateral olfactory stria travels without interruption across the limen insulae and into the uncus, parahippocampal gyrus and part of the amygdaloid body. The sense of smell is the only sense which does not relay in the thalamus.

The Limbic System

It is useful to list the components of the limbic system and these fall naturally into two groups, the nerve cell components and the pathways.

The *nerve cell components* are:
1. The medial olfactory area;
2. The indusium griseum which is a remnant of the hippocampus and which lies on the superior surface of the corpus callosum;
3. The cingulate gyrus;
4. The parahippocampal gyrus;
5. The hippocampus;
6. The amygdaloid body;
7. The insular cortex;
8. The dentate gyrus and the gyrus fasciolaris;
9. The mamillary bodies.

The *pathways* are:
1. The fornix;
2. The mamillothalamic tract;
3. The mamillotegmental tract;
4. The stria medullaris thalami;
5. The stria terminalis;
6. The cingulum, already encountered as a bundle of association fibres;
7. The anterior commissure;
8. The medial forebrain bundle;

9.   The medial and lateral longitudinal striae.

The nerve cell components and the pathways will now be considered together.

The hippocampus, an inrolled area of cortex, lies in the floor of the inferior horn of the lateral ventricle and is composed largely of cells whose axonic processes form a white layer on its surface called the alveus. This passes to the medial border of the hippocampus and becomes continuous with the fimbria (Fig. 79). The fimbria of the hippocampi pass backwards and become the crura of the fornix which are flat in cross-section. The crura of the fornix are joined together by the commissure of the fornix.

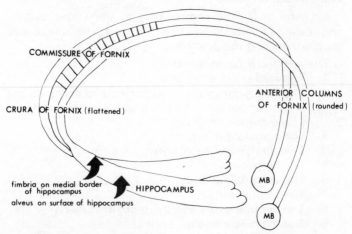

Fig. 79. Hippocampi and fornix. MB=mamillary body.

Anteriorly, above the roof of the third ventricle, the two crura come together in the median plane to form the body of the fornix. Above the interventricular foramina the body of the fornix diverges into the right and left columns which are rounded in cross-section and which terminate in the mamillary bodies. Fibres leaving the hippocampus pass to the opposite hippocampus via the commissure of the fornix, to the anterior hypothalamic area and the medial olfactory area, to the mamillary body, and to the anterior nucleus of the thalamus directly.

The dentate gyrus lies under the fimbria of the hippo-campus and, traced anteriorly it is indistinguishable from the uncus; traced posteriorly it separates from the fimbria to become continuous with the gyrus fasciolaris at the region of the splenium of the corpus callosum. The gyrus fasciolaris then becomes continuous with the indusium griseum which lies on the superior surface of the corpus callosum and in which are embedded the medial and lateral longitudinal striae constituting its white fibres which terminate in the medial olfactory area. Some authorities think that this latter pathway is afferent to the hippo-campus.

The stria terminalis passes from the amygdaloid body to the grey matter around the anterior commissure. It passes over the superior aspect of the thalamus with the thalamo-striate vein.

. The stria medullaris thalami of each side pass from the medial olfactory area to the habenular nuclei which lie in the root of the pineal body. From the habenular nuclei fibres arise which pass to the interpeduncular nuclei which are part of the midbrain reticular formation (see Chapter XVI).

The mamillothalamic and mamillotegmental tracts are self-explanatory.

The medial forebrain bundle contains ascending and descending fibres which connect the medial olfactory area with hypothalamic areas and with the tegmentum of the midbrain.

It is not possible to describe the circuitry of the limbic system in a definite way because it is not yet clear, in most cases, in which direction the impulses are travelling.

Functions of the Limbic System

Only a small part of the oldest region of the cortex is concerned with the sense of olfaction, that is, the uncus, the limen insulae, the parahippocampal gyrus and part of the amygdaloid body. Man has a poor sense of smell but has absolutely and relatively the largest hippocampi in the animal kingdom. It is now believed that the limbic system is to do with mood (affect). The hippocampal projection via the fornix to the thalamus may be responsible for changes in muscle tone which accompany emotional states, e.g. tense with rage or weak with laughter. Animal experiments have shown that ablation of the amygdaloid body results in rage and that damage of the temporal lobes can result in a loss of the sense of fear and a marked increase in sexual behaviour sometimes directed inappropriately.

In man, clinically, it has been found that:

1. Neurons in the hippocampus are very susceptible to toxic agents or hypoxia;

2. Bilateral destruction of the hippocampus results in the inability to retain new information. Memory for remote events is usually unaffected and such individuals may still retain intellectual functions but be quite unable to learn new facts and skills. In some cases of senile dementia, characterised by memory loss, the most prominent lesions are found in the hippocampus;

3. Damage to the temporal lobe near the uncus or the anterior part of the parahippocampal gyrus results in uncinate fits which start with olfactory hallucinations and are followed by a sense of unreality.

Finally, it is believed that the limbic cortex is connected with the reticular formation and it is proposed that this connection is important in the alerting process (Chapter XVI).

THE RETICULAR FORMATION

General

The reticular formation of the nervous system is defined as that part which is not already occupied by groups of nerve cell bodies with specific functions or by definitive tracts. There is disagreement about whether the term 'reticular formation' should be restricted to the brain stem or should be used in a wider sense to include all known reticular regions at all levels of the neuraxis. The general characteristic of the reticular formation is that it is an intimate and diffuse mixture of nerve cells and their processes. The reticular formation receives data from most sensory systems and has efferent connections with all levels of the neuraxis and this has led some investigators, e.g. Brodal, to describe ascending and descending reticular systems. The cerebral cortex has direct connections with the reticular formation. It is difficult to analyse the reticular formation because the neurons of which it consists are not arranged in well-defined groups. Almost all reticular axons extend rostrally and caudally and have many branching collaterals. Neuroanatomical studies have shown that the reticular formation is a polyneural pathway and because of this the usual experimental methods of following pathways are frustrated.

The Reticular Formation of the Medulla Oblongata

The medullary reticular formation consists of three main masses of cell bodies:

1. *The paramedian group*—At the level of the midpoint of the inferior olivary nucleus and dorsal to it there

are groups of cells present near the midline. These reticular neurons send most of their fibres to the cerebellum.

2. *The central group*—This group of cells lies dorsal to the inferior olivary nucleus and makes up about two-thirds of the reticular formation. The cells are considered to be the 'effector' area which corresponds to the descending reticular formation of Brodal.

3. *The lateral group*—One of the areas of cells making up the lateral group of reticular nuclei lies at the level of the great sensory decussation. The other area lies medial to the spinal nucleus of the fifth nerve, ventral to the vestibular nuclear complex. This lateral group is smaller than the central group and is considered to be the 'sensory' part because it receives many collateral fibres from the secondary neurons of the sensory pathways.

The Reticular Formation of the Pons

The pontine reticular formation has the same three divisions as the medullary reticular formation but the 'sensory' part is smaller and obvious only in the caudal pons. The reticular formation lies in the tegmental part of the pons.

The Reticular Formation of the Midbrain

The midbrain reticular formation is less extensive than the pontine reticular formation lying caudal to it. The red nucleus of the midbrain is now recognised by many neuroanatomists as a definitive part of the reticular formation and it is under the direct influence of the cerebral cortex via corticorubral fibres. The mesencephalic reticular nuclei consist of scattered cells in an area bounded by the medial lemnisci, red nuclei and the tectum of the midbrain. Part of the reticular formation of the midbrain is the interpeduncular nucleus which receives fibres from the habenular nuclei via the fasciculus retroflexus (Fig. 78).

Cerebellar Connections of the Reticular Formation

The reticular formation of the medulla oblongata receives sensory fibres from the spinal cord and efferents enter the cerebellum via the inferior cerebellar peduncle so that an additional pathway for transmission of general sensory information to the cerebellum is established.

Descending Influences of the Reticular Formation

Electrophysiological studies in animals have shown that stimulation of the ventromedial part of the reticular formation of the medulla oblongata inhibits or reduces most forms of motor activity. All inhibitory effects were bilateral. No inhibitory effects were found on stimulation of the most lateral part of the medullary reticular formation. A larger area of the reticular formation facilitates or augments reflexes at lower levels and this area extends rostrally through the pons and mid-brain and into the diencephalon.

The reticular formation has influences on breathing, causing inspiration or expiration depending on the area stimulated. Vasomotor effects can also be elicited by stimulation of the reticular formation and the primary vasomotor centre is situated in the reticular formation of the medulla oblongata. The medulla oblongata pressor and depressor areas provide a central mechanism which reflexly regulates the blood pressure and heart rate.

Ascending Influences of the Reticular Formation.

The brain stem reticular formation can act in a rostral direction and thus influence the cerebral cortex with resultant changes in the latter's electrical activity. The cerebral cortex shows different patterns of electrical activity (electroencephalograms) depending on whether the individual is asleep or alert. It has been shown by animal experiments that an animal whose neural axis has been sectioned at a high spinal level shows an electroencephalogram characteristic of the waking state and when the section is at the midbrain level the electroencephalogram is typical of the sleeping state. The con-clusion drawn from these facts was that the lower brain stem has some effect on alertness but how this could be brought about by the normal pathways was not clear. It was therefore suggested that, as well as the normal ascending sensory pathways, a second ascending system was present which exerted a powerful influence on vast regions of the cerebral cortex. This second ascending system is now known as the ascending reticular activating system.

The reticular formation receives sensory information from the spinoreticular tracts, from the lateral spinothalamic tracts via collaterals, from the nucleus of the tractus soli-tarius, the spinal part of the trigeminal nerve, the vestibu-lar nuclei, the superior colliculi and the cerebellum. It also receives sensory information from the viscera. It probably does not receive impulses from the posterior columns of the spinal cord or from the medial lemnisci. Many of the ascending fibres run in the central tegmental tracts.

The reticular activating system must be compared with the lemniscal system. Information carried by the lemniscal system is interpreted in a highly specific and discriminatory manner. The reticular activating system is non-specific and it provides, at best, only a vague awareness of any particular sensation. The cortex is stimulated by the reticu-lar activating system in a general way giving a profound effect on the waking state and on alerting reactions to sensory stimuli. In the conscious state the information reaching the cortex via the reticular activating system sharpens attentiveness and creates optimum conditions for the perception of sensory data conveyed by the lemniscal system. The route to the cerebral cortex seems likely to involve the non-specific nuclei of the thalamus as well as the central, intralaminar and reticular nuclei (see Chapter XVII).

The Clinical Importance of the Reticular Formation

The function of the reticular activating system is affected

by certain commonly used drugs. Under barbiturate medication and some anaesthetics the transmission through the reticular formation is suppressed whereas transmission continues by the lemniscal route. Many drugs have a tranquillising effect or produce unconsciousness by impeding transmission in the polysynaptic reticular activating system passing through the brain stem. Damage to the reticular formation in man usually brings about a prolonged coma. Damage to the lower brain stem is a very serious event as the reticular formation in this situation is concerned with the vital functions, that is, the breathing rhythm and the control of heart rate and blood pressure.

CHAPTER XVII

THE THALAMI

General Topography

The thalami lie on either side of the midline with the cavity of the third ventricle lying between them. They are relay stations for sensations travelling to the cerebral cortex with the exception of the sense of smell.

Each thalamus seen from above (Fig. 80) is egg-shaped with the smaller end pointing forwards and the two medial borders parallel. The lateral borders of the large posterior ends are widely divergent and the posterior ends are called the pulvinars. Each pulvinar overhangs two rounded projections, the medial and lateral geniculate bodies which are also part of the thalamus. The anterior extremity of the thalamus is the anterior tubercle and it forms the posterior boundary of the interventricular foramen. (The anterior boundary of the interventricular foramen is formed by the rounded column of the fornix.)

The medial surfaces of the thalami are covered by ependyma and form the lateral walls of the third ventricle. Often an interthalamic adhesion is present which bridges across the cavity of the third ventricle.

The superior surface of the thalamus is limited laterally by the stria terminalis and the thalamostriate vein which separate the thalamus from the caudate nucleus. There is a groove coursing obliquely across the superior surface of the thalamus which houses the fornix and thus divides the superior surface into medial and lateral parts. The lateral part forms part of the floor of the lateral ventricle and is therefore covered with ependyma. The medial part is covered by the

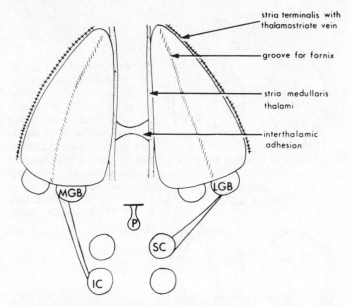

Fig. 80. The thalami from above. P=pineal body; MGB=medial geniculate body; IC=inferior colliculus; LGB=lateral geniculate body; SC=superior colliculus.

tela choroidea of the third ventricle and between the lateral edge of the fornix and the upper surface of the thalamus the lateral margin of the tela choroidea is invaginated into the lateral ventricle through the choroid fissure (see Chapter XIV). The junction between the superior surface and the medial surface is demarcated by the stria medullaris thalami.

The inferior surface rests on the hypothalamus and the posterior part of the inferior surface shows the medial and lateral geniculate bodies.

The superior and lateral surfaces of the thalamus are covered by thin layers of white matter. The superior layer is the stratum zonale and the lateral layer is called the external medullary lamina (Fig. 81).

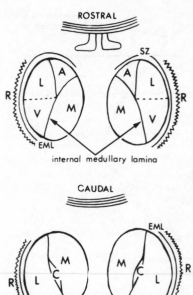

Fig. 81. Coronal sections of the thalamus. A=anterior group of nuclei; L=lateral group of nuclei; M=medial group of nuclei; V=ventral group of nuclei; R=thalamic reticular nucleus; SZ=stratum zonale; EML=external medullary lamina; C=central and intralaminar nuclei; LGB=lateral geniculate body; MGB=medial geniculate body.

Thalamic Nuclei

The thalamus can be divided into groups of nuclei, some having specific connections and some not. The interior of the thalamus is divided by the diagonally placed internal medullary lamina which splits rostrally to enclose the anterior thalamic nuclei and caudally to enclose the central nucleus and the intralaminar nuclei. The external medullary lamina is separated from the internal capsule (lying lateral to the thalamus) by the thalamic reticular nucleus. Medial to the internal medullary lamina lies the medial group of thalamic nuclei. Two groups of nuclei lie lateral to the internal medullary lamina; laterally and below the ventral group, and laterally and above the lateral group. The ventral group peters out caudally so that the lateral group forms the posterior part of the thalamus. This means that the pulvinar is part of the lateral group of thalamic nuclei although some authorities call the pulvinar the posterior group.

The medial geniculate bodies lie in the angles between the inferior surfaces of the thalami, the lateral aspects of the midbrain and the dorsal surfaces of the crura cerebri. The medial geniculate bodies receive the brachia of the inferior colliculi which convey auditory impulses.

The lateral geniculate bodies are continuous with the lateral parts of the optic tracts. They form the thalamic termination of the optic fibres and they give rise to the fibres of the optic radiations by which means the visual impulses are conveyed to the occipital lobes. Some fibres bypass the lateral geniculate bodies and enter the supero-lateral margins of the superior colliculi; such fibres are concerned solely with visual reflexes.

The Connections of the Thalami

The thalamic nuclei may be divided into two main groups. One group receives projections from specific parts of the neuraxis and projects the information to well-defined cortical areas. These nuclei are the specific thalamic relay nuclei. The other group are the association nuclei and they do not receive fibres directly from the ascending systems but have abundant connections with other nuclei. These association nuclei of the thalami project to the association areas of the cerebral cortex. The association areas of the cortex are those areas from which no motor response is elicited on stimulation and to which sensory information is not primarily relayed. They are present in man and primates only. By means of the association cortex it is thought that an individual has access to current sensory experience which can be compared with a repository of data derived from previous experience.

Each group of nuclei of the thalamus will now be considered in turn and its connections outlined.

Specific Thalamic Nuclei

1. Anterior group. This group receives the mamillo-

thalamic tract and projects to the cingulate gyrus (see Chapter XV).

2. Ventral group. This group receives fibres from part of the basal ganglia (specifically the globus pallidus), the cerebellum, the lateral spinothalamic tract and the medial lemniscus. It also receives secondary trigeminal fibres and secondary taste fibres. The ventral group projects to the corpus striatum and the frontal and parietal lobes.

3. The central and intralaminar group receives information from other thalamic nuclei and from the reticular system and projects to the corpus striatum and most of the cortex. It is the group of nuclei which is believed to participate in cortical arousal.

4. The reticular group. The reticular group of thalamic nuclei lies outside the main body of the thalamus and is continuous with the remainder of the reticular system. It receives fibres from other thalamic nuclei, the brain stem, the reticular formation and the cortex and it projects to the cortex and the midbrain.

5. The medial geniculate body. This nucleus receives auditory information and relays it to the auditory cortex.

6. The lateral geniculate body. This nucleus receives the optic tract fibres and relays them to the calcarine cortex.

Non-specific Thalamic Nuclei

1. Medial group. This group has integrative functions. It receives fibres from other thalamic nuclei, from the basal ganglia (see Chapter XIX) and from the frontal cortex and it projects to the frontal association area which is sometimes called the prefrontal region. The prefrontal region is needed for activities which are rather difficult to evaluate such as mature judgement, abstract thinking, tactfulness, forebearance and foresight.

2. The lateral group. These association nuclei receive fibres from other thalamic nuclei and from the parietal lobe and project to the parietal lobe.

CHAPTER XVIII

THE OPTIC PATHWAY, VISUAL REFLEXES AND EYE MOVEMENTS

The Optic Pathway

The visual pathway starts in the light-sensitive region of the eyeball, the retina, from which impulses are carried from the photoreceptors by means of three neurons, two of which lie within the retina, to the occipital cortex of the cerebral hemispheres.

Light entering the eyeball impinges on the retina which has developed as an evaginated portion of the brain, the optic vesicle (Fig. 82), which becomes by invagination the optic cup, having an inner layer and an outer layer. The cavity of the optic vesicle is obliterated by the opposition of the inner and outer layers of the optic cup which results in the retina consisting of two layers. The outer layer of the optic cup gives rise to pigmented epithelium which reduces the scattering of light within the eye. The inner layer differentiates into the neural portion of the retina (Fig. 83), which has the following layers:

1. The receptor layer which lies adjacent to the pigment cells and consists of two types of cells whose peripheral processes are modified to form rods and cones, the photoreceptors;

2. An intermediate cell layer containing bipolar cells (the first neuron of the optic pathway) and association neurons of two types called horizontal and amacrine cells;

3. An inner cell layer containing ganglion cells which are the second neuron on the optic pathway.

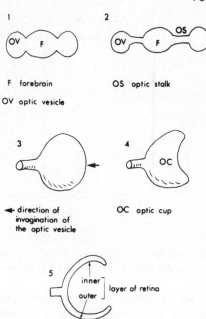

Fig. 82. Development of the optic cup.

The rods are used for vision in dim light and the cones in bright light and for colour discrimination. Impulses from the rods and cones are transmitted to the bipolar cells and from the latter to the ganglion cells. The axons of the ganglion cells make up the so-called 'optic nerve' which is not a true nerve but a fibre tract connecting two parts of the brain. The association neurons modify impulse transmission in the retina. The processes of the horizontal cells cannot be positively identified as either axons or dendrites and it may be possible for each process to receive or to transmit signals. Amacrine cells have only one process which makes contact with bipolar cells, with other amacrine cells and with the cell bodies and dendrites of ganglion cells.

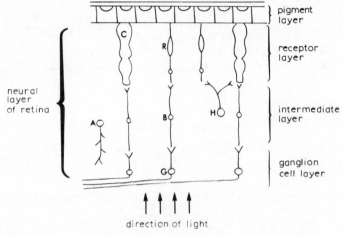

Fig. 83. Section of retina. R=rod; C=cone; B=bipolar cell; H= horizontal cell; A=amacrine cell; G=ganglion cell.

At the posterior pole of the eyeball is the macula lutea and in the centre of it is a depression called the fovea centralis. The depression is present because the inner layers of the retina have been pushed aside so that light has direct access to the photoreceptors with no neural components of the retina intervening. The fovea centralis of the retina is composed entirely of closely packed cones and when vision is directed at an object the optical axis of each eye is so moved that the centre of the object's image on each retina falls on the fovea centralis which is the area of most acute vision and of colour discrimination.

The axons of the ganglion cells are unmyelinated and they converge on the optic disc which lies to the medial side of the posterior pole of the eyeball. The fibres are heaped up as they converge on the optic disc and this area of the eye is blind because no photoreceptors are present. On emerging from the eyeball the axons of the ganglion cells acquire a myelin sheath.

The optic nerves enter the cranial cavity through the optic foramina and unite to form the optic chiasma, beyond which they continue as the optic tracts (Fig. 84). There is a partial decussation in the optic chiasma as fibres arising from the nasal parts of the retina cross in the optic chiasma to terminate in the contralateral lateral geniculate body, while fibres arising from the temporal parts of the retina terminate in the ipsilateral lateral geniculate body. In binocular vision images fall upon portions of both retinae. The images of objects on the right hand side of an individual are projected onto the nasal part of the retina of the right eye and the temporal part of the retina of the left eye. In the chiasma the fibres from these two retinal portions are combined to form the left optic tract, which carries impulses representing the complete picture impinging on the left halves of the two retinae.

The optic tracts begin at the posterolateral corners of the optic chiasma and sweep round the hypothalamus and rostral parts of the crura cerebri. Most of the fibres of the optic tract terminate in the lateral geniculate body but some leave the tract rostral to its principal termination in the lateral geniculate body and project to the superior colliculi and the pretectal region which lies immediately rostral to the superior colliculi.

The geniculocalcarine tracts arise from the lateral geniculate bodies and form the optic radiations which end in the calcarine (striate) cortex on the medial surfaces of the occipital lobes. The cells within the lateral geniculate bodies are the third neurons on the optic pathway. The fibres connected with the inferior quadrants of the retina loop forwards into the temporal lobes before turning backwards. This part of the geniculocalcarine tract is called Meyer's loop.

The retinal areas have a precise point-to-point relationship with the lateral geniculate bodies; fibres (excluding macular fibres) from the upper retinal quadrants end in the anteromedial part of the lateral geniculate body, fibres from the lower retinal quadrants (excluding macular fibres)

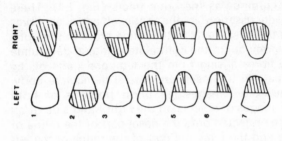

FIELD DEFECTS (shaded) CAUSED BY LESIONS AT THE NUMBERED REGIONS.

Fig. 84. The optic pathway.

end in the anterolateral part of the lateral geniculate body. The macular fibres end in the relatively large central and posterior regions of the lateral geniculate body. A similar point-to-point relationship exists between the lateral geniculate body and the calcarine cortex. Fibres from the anteromedial part of the lateral geniculate body (upper retinal quadrants) project to the superior lip of the calcarine sulcus and those from the anterolateral part of the lateral geniculate body (lower retinal quadrants) project to the inferior lip of the calcarine sulcus. The macular fibres terminate in the posterior third of the calcarine sulcus. The portions of the lateral geniculate body and the calcarine cortex for the macular region are large relative to the areas for the rest of the retina because that area of the retina is the part concerned with acute vision.

Lesions of the Optic Pathway

Figure 84 outlines the results, in terms of field defects, of interruption of the optic pathway in seven places. Note that the temporal *fields* project onto the nasal parts of the retina and that the nasal *fields* project onto the temporal parts of the retina. The most likely cause of some of the lesions shown is as follows:

Lesion 1. Severence of the optic nerve;

Lesion 2. Tumour of the pituitary gland;

Lesion 3. Lateral pressure on the optic chiasma due to aneurysm of the internal carotid artery.

Lesion 5. Tumour or trauma of the temporal lobe.

The Superior Colliculi

The superior colliculi receive fibres from:

1. The retinae, via the optic tracts;
2. The cerebral cortex;
3. The spinal cord;
4. The inferior colliculi.

The fibres from the retinae have been mentioned previously. The corticotectal fibres arise from parts of the frontal, temporal, parietal and occipital lobes. The cortex of the occipital lobe is the most important source of afferent fibres to the superior colliculus in man. The part of the occipital cortex which projects to the superior colliculus lies adjacent to the primary visual cortex on which the geniculocalcarine tract has projected.

Other afferents to the superior colliculus indicate its role as a sensory integrative centre in lower animals. Fibres from the inferior colliculus convey impulses of cochlear origin and spinotectal fibres convey information from general sensory endings so that reflex connections are established for directing the eyes and head towards the source of auditory and cutaneous stimuli.

Efferents from the superior colliculi travel to the spinal cord, nuclei of the brain stem, red nuclei, substantia nigra and reticular formation. It is thought that there is a projection to the cerebellum by means of tectopontine fibres.

The Light Reflex

When light is shone onto the retina of one eye both pupils constrict. The response in the eye stimulated is the direct pupillary light reflex and the constriction of the pupil of the other eye is the consensual pupillary light reflex.

The anatomical pathways mediating these reflexes are as follows: Impulses due to the light stimulation pass along the optic nerve and optic tract to the pretectal region (rostral to the superior colliculi). The axons of the pretectal neurons partially cross in the posterior commissure so that each pretectal region terminates bilaterally on the Edinger-Westphal nuclei (parasympathetic). Preganglionic fibres course in the third cranial nerves and synapse in the ciliary ganglia and postganglionic fibres pass from the ciliary ganglia to the sphincter pupillae muscles of the two eyes.

The Accommodation Reflex

The eyes are adapted to see objects clearly at infinity. In practical terms this means that the eye is 'at rest' when viewing objects at a distance of six metres or more when the optical axes are parallel. To see an object clearly at a closer distance than six metres it is necessary to accommodate. During accommodation three changes take place:

1. The eyes converge so that the optical axes meet at the object;
2. The ciliary muscles contract which allows the elastic lens to assume its natural state in which its surfaces are more bi-convex and its refractive power greater;
3. The pupils constrict to increase the depth of focus.

It is assumed that in this reflex the visual impulses pass to the visual cortex in the normal way and are then relayed to the brain-stem centres, that is, the oculomotor complex. Either the impulses are relayed from the visual association cortex to the brain stem via the fibres in the brachium of the superior colliculus or they are relayed via the superior longitudinal association tract to the frontal cortex and thence by corticobulbar fibres to the oculomotor complex of nuclei.

The pathways for the light and the accommodation reflex must be different as the two reflexes may become dissociated on some diseases. In syphilis of the central nervous system the eye responds in all three respects to accommodation but no pupillary constriction is obtained in response to light. This is called the Argyll Robertson pupil.

Eye Movements

The eyes are moved in the orbit by the extraocular muscles and their function is to manipulate the optical axes so that the image of the object falls on the appropriate region of each retina. All ocular movements in whatever direction, horizontal, vertical or rotatory, require reciprocal activity of the extraocular muscles. The fibres of the medial longitudinal fasciculus serve to interconnect the three cranial nerves involved in the motor control of the extraocular muscles and they also carry a large component from the vestibular nuclei. The co-ordination of eye movements with those of the head is dependent on the data received by the third, fourth and sixth cranial nerves from the vestibular nuclei which relay sensory information from the balancing apparatus of the inner ear via the medial longitudinal fasciculus.

The vestibular control of the extraocular muscles is only part of the neural mechanism acting to bring about movements of the eyes. There is also the frontal eye field for voluntary scanning movements and the visual association cortex for automatic scanning movements. The precise synchronisation of ocular movements is controlled by the brain stem, mainly through fibres of the medial longitudinal fasciculus which contains fibres from the vestibular nuclei as mentioned above and also internuncial neurons connecting the three nuclei supplying the extraocular muscles. Conjugate eye movements cannot be dissociated voluntarily and this suggests that the corticobulbar system acts on the internuncial cells which in turn integrate the motor neurons activating the extraocular muscles.

Nystagmus is a term applied to rhythmic oscillation of the eyes. One phase of the oscillation is usually more prolonged than the other and is called the slow component. The shorter phase is referred to as the quick component and, clinically, nystagmus is described as being in the direction of the quick component. The slow phase of nystagmus is initiated by the semicircular canals of the balancing apparatus of the inner ear and the fast phase is due to an unknown central mechanism. The phenomenon of nystagmus can be used to test the function of the semicircular canals either by causing conduction currents in the fluid (caloric test) or by rotating the patient in a Barany chair and then observing the eye movements.

CHAPTER XIX

THE DEEP GREY MASSES OF THE CEREBRAL HEMISPHERES, THE INTERNAL CAPSULE AND THE EXTRAPYRAMIDAL SYSTEM

The Deep Grey Masses of the Cerebral Hemispheres

The deep grey masses of the cerebral hemispheres, comprising the caudate nucleus, lentiform nucleus, amygdaloid body (nucleus) and the claustrum, are collectively called the basal ganglia. The amygdaloid body and caudate nucleus have already been seen in their relationship to the lateral ventricle (see Chapter XIV).

Initially, the future caudate nucleus, lentiform nucleus and thalamus form a common mass of grey matter but in the course of development projection fibres grow obliquely through this to form the internal capsule, with the result that the thalamus and head and body of the caudate nucleus lie on the medial side of the internal capsule and the lentiform nucleus lateral to it. This separation is complete except anteroinferiorly where the head of the caudate nucleus and the anterior part of the lentiform nucleus are still joined. The structures shown in Figure 85, with the exception of the thalamus, make up the basal ganglia.

The lentiform nucleus is subdivided into three parts, an outer segment called the putamen and two inner segments called the globus pallidus. The claustrum is a thin plate of

A Primer of Human Neuroanatomy

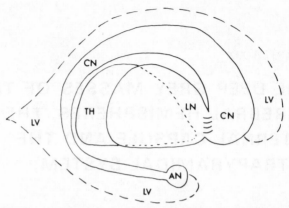

Fig. 85. The deep grey masses of the cerebral hemispheres. TH=
thalamus; CN=caudate nucleus; AN=amygdaloid nucleus or
body; LN=lentiform nucleus; LV=lateral ventricle.

grey matter lying close to the outer surface of the lentiform
nucleus. The putamen of the lentiform nucleus and the
head of the caudate nucleus are connected by a number
of bridges of grey matter.

The corpus striatum is composed of the caudate nucleus
and the lentiform nucleus. The *striatum* is made up of the
caudate nucleus and the putamen of the lentiform nucleus.
The phylogenetic terms refer to the following groups of
structures:

Archistriatum   amygdaloid body
Paleostriatum   globus pallidus
Neostriatum   striatum (Caudate nucleus and
                                         putamen)

The globus pallidus is often called the pallidum.

Figure 86 shows the structures in horizontal section and
demonstrates the shape of the lentiform nucleus. The
Λ-shaped area in the section X-X is the internal capsule
and in the section Y-Y the anterior part of the internal
capsule is interrupted by grey bands joining the head of
the caudate nucleus to the putamen of the lentiform
nucleus. The claustrum can be seen as a thin band of

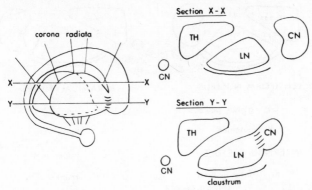

Fig. 86. The deep grey masses of the cerebral hemispheres in horizontal section. TH=thalamus; CN=caudate nucleus; LN= lentiform nucleus.

grey matter lateral to the lentiform nucleus. The fibres passing between the thalamus and the lentiform nucleus and between the caudate nucleus and the lentiform nucleus are the projection fibres of the cerebral hemispheres. Where the projection fibres are tightly packed together they form the internal capsule but where they diverge superiorly they form the corona radiata, the fibres of which have to intersect the commissural fibres in passing to or from the cerebral cortex. If the internal capsules are followed inferiorly the fibres are found to be closely grouped together to form the crura cerebri.

In horizontal section the internal capsule is angled (Fig. 87) because it is moulded on the medial surface of the lentiform nucleus but it is also applied to its posterior end. The internal capsule is described as having an anterior limb or lenticulocaudate part, a bend or genu and a posterior limb or thalamolentiform part. Lying posterior to the lentiform nucleus is the retrolentiform part of the internal capsule and inferiorly is the sublentiform part.

The anterior limb carries fibres travelling from the frontal cortex to the nuclei of the pons and thalamocortical fibres travelling from the thalamus to the frontal cortex. The

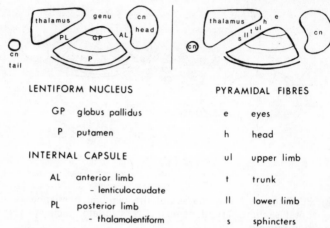

Fig. 87. Horizontal sections showing internal capsule.

genu contains corticobulbar and corticoreticular fibres.

The posterior limb in its anterior half or two-thirds contains corticobulbar and corticospinal fibres. These fibres are arranged in a particular way with the body represented as indicated. The remainder of the internal capsule is occupied mainly by general and special sensory fibres. Lying close to the fibres for sphincter control are the thalamocortical fibres ascending to the postcentral gyrus and in the retrolentiform and sublentiform parts of the internal capsule are the optic and auditory radiations. See Chapter XIII for a consideration of the tapetum of the corpus callosum and its relationship to the internal capsule.

Scattered in the posterior limb are temporopontine and parietopontine fibres. Fibres concerned with the connections of the corpus striatum are found throughout the internal capsule.

The basal ganglia are supplied by the central branches of the middle cerebral artery. The medial striate artery ascends through the lentiform nucleus, caudate nucleus and the internal capsule. The lateral striate artery ascends over the lower part of the lateral surface of the lentiform nucleus and then traverses the lentiform nucleus to reach the caudate nucleus. Haemorrhage or thrombosis of these central branches will have a devastating effect because of the close grouping together of the projection fibres.

The Extrapyramidal System

It is difficult to define the so-called extrapyramidal system. It should consist of all centres and tracts, exclusive of the pyramidal system, that have a significant influence on somatic motor functions. Most neuroanatomists agree that the system includes the corpus striatum, the subthalamus, the substantia nigra, the red nucleus and the brain-stem reticular formation. The cerebellum must also be included together with such pathways as the reticulospinal, rubrospinal, vestibulospinal and tectospinal tracts which are able to influence the anterior horn cells directly. The extrapyramidal system is phylogenetically older than the corticospinal system and it is defined using the pyramidal system as a reference although the latter is present only in mammals. In submammalian forms of animals the diencephalon and corpus striatum together constitute the highest sensorimotor integrating mechanism of the forebrain. In mammals the functions of the corpus striatum become subordinate to those of the cortex. The centres giving rise to some of the tracts of the extrapyramidal system, namely the red nucleus and the reticular formation of the brain stem, are directly influenced by the cortex.

The corpus striatum comes under the influence of the cerebral cortex and thalamus and the afferent fibres end mainly in the caudate nucleus and the putamen (Fig. 88). Corticostriate fibres originate in wide areas of cortex, especially in the frontal and parietal lobes including areas from which corticospinal fibres arise. Most fibres travel in the internal capsule but some travel in the external capsule (between the lentiform nucleus and the claustrum) to reach the putamen. Most of the fibres leaving the

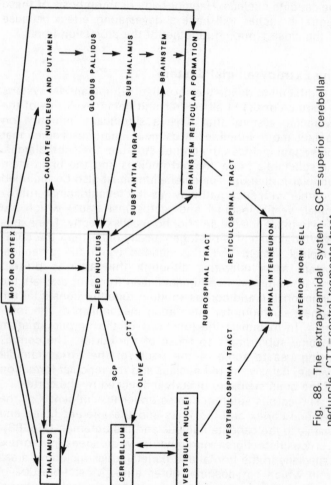

Fig. 88. The extrapyramidal system. SCP=superior cerebellar peduncle; CTT=central tegmental tract.

caudate nucleus and the putamen end in the globus pallidus.

Efferent fibres from the globus pallidus form two main bundles:

1. The lenticular fasciculus;
2. The ansa lenticularis.

The above bundles project to the subthalamus which is a transitional zone inferior to the thalamus, medial to the internal capsule and caudal to the hypothalamus. Nuclei found within the subthalamus include the subthalamic nucleus, the zona incerta and the nuclei of the tegmental fields of Forel. The lenticular fasciculus traverses the inferior parts of the internal capsule and enters the subthalamus but the ansa lenticularis fibres sweep ventromedially and rostrally around the posterior limb of the internal capsule and thence to the subthalamus. In addition, fibres arise from the globus pallidus and pass to the substantia nigra. From the subthalamus fibres travel to the substantia nigra, the tegmental nuclei of the brain stem and the brain stem reticular formation.

The substantia nigra has connections with the corpus striatum, red nucleus and reticular formation and there are many corticonigral afferents from the frontal, parietal and occipital lobes. The substantia nigra first appears in mammals along with the neocortex and is especially well developed in the human brain.

The red nucleus and the reticular formation of the brain stem have many connections in common, including direct connections with the cerebral cortex; the red nucleus is usually recognised now as a specialised part of the mesencephalic reticular formation. The red nucleus receives some afferents from the cerebellum via the superior cerebellar peduncle. Many of the fibres from the superior cerebellar peduncle merely traverse the red nucleus and do not terminate within it. It is thought that some fibres from the red nucleus terminate in the thalamus. Efferent fibres from the red nucleus travel in the central tegmental tract to the inferior olivary nucleus and thence to the cerebellum. The central tegmental tract also includes fibres ascending from the reticular formation of the brain stem to the diencephalon. Caudally running fibres emerge from the red nucleus and travel to the brain stem reticular formation (the rubroreticular tracts) and to the spinal cord above midthoracic level (the rubrospinal tracts). The rubroreticular and rubrospinal tracts decussate immediately on leaving the nucleus in the ventral tegmental decussation. It is thought that rubroreticular and reticulospinal connections are probably more important in man than the rubrospinal tracts.

The cerebellum is involved in the extrapyramidal system in order to provide a circuit which ensures smoothly co-ordinated muscle action in voluntary movements. Cortico-pontine fibres from all cerebral lobes terminate in the pontine nuclei of the same side. Pontocerebellar fibres then project to the contralateral cerebellar cortex and fibres pass from the cortex to the dentate nucleus. The efferent outflow from the dentate nucleus constitutes most of the fibres in the superior cerebellar peduncle and the fibres decussate at the level of the inferior colliculi and continue rostrally to the red nucleus where some synapse and then travel to the thalamus but most pass directly to the thalamus. The circuit is completed by the thalamic projections to the cerebral cortex.

The vestibular nuclei receive afferents from the vestibular apparatus and from the archicerebellum (see Chapter IX), and vestibulospinal fibres pass down in the spinal cord as the vestibulospinal tract and the sulcomarginal fasciculus.

Summary of the Extrapyramidal System

An understanding of the inter-relationships between the pyramidal and extrapyramidal motor systems has gradually evolved during this century. It would be incorrect to demarcate sharply these two systems as lesions in man rarely damage the pyramidal pathway without simultaneous involvement of extrapyramidal connections. Also it is thought possible that the pyramidal system does not initiate all voluntary, non-stereotyped movement and that some voluntary movement is mediated by the extrapyramidal system. Perhaps the pyramidal system improves the speed and agility of voluntary muscle movement. Pyramidal tract section is less devastating than would be supposed if it is assumed that the pyramidal tract were the only voluntary motor system.

The corpus striatum does not project fibres directly to spinal levels but does send fibres to the motor cortex via the thalamus. It is likely, therefore, that the contribution of the corpus striatum to motor functions must be mediated by cortical motor neurons which project to spinal levels via the corticospinal tract. This would correlate with the observation that fibres from the primary motor area con-stitute only 40 per cent of the fibres of the pyramidal tract, the remainder originating in other areas of the frontal cortex and in the cortex of the parietal lobe.

CHAPTER XX

THE HYPOTHALAMUS

General

The hypothalamus forms the lateral wall of the third ventricle, inferior to the hypothalamic sulcus (Fig. 89). On the ventral surface of the brain the infundibulum, to which is attached the hypophysis cerebri, emerges posterior to the optic chiasma. Posterior to the infundibulum is the tuber cinereum and posterior to that are the mamillary bodies. The hypothalamus extends from the optic chiasma to the caudal border of the mamillary bodies where it becomes continuous with the tegmentum of the midbrain. The descending columns of the fornix divide the hypothalamus into medial and lateral parts.

The Lateral Part of the Hypothalamus

The lateral hypothalamic area is bounded medially by the mamillothalamic tract and the anterior column of the fornix. The medial edge of the internal capsule and the subthalamic region form its lateral boundary. The cells of the lateral part of the hypothalamus are interspersed with longitudinally running fibres passing to or from the hypothalamic nuclei or merely passing through the area. One definite tract found in the lateral part of the hypothalamus is the medial forebrain bundle. The cells of origin of the medial forebrain bundle lie in the medial olfactory area (see Chapter XV) and this bundle runs caudally giving off fibres to the hypothalamic nuclei and to the reticular formation of the midbrain. The fibres just described are related to basic emotional drives and also to the sense of smell.

MEDIAN SAGITTAL SECTION

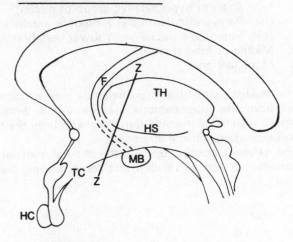

SECTION Z – Z

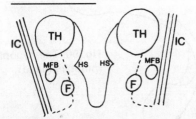

Fig. 89. Position of the hypothalamus. TH=thalamus; F=fornix; MB=mamillary body; TC=tuber cinereum; HC=hypophysis cerebri; IC=internal capsule; MFB=medial forebrain bundle; HS=hypothalamic sulcus. The dotted line in the section Z-Z indicates the boundary between the medial and lateral parts of the hypothalamus.

The Medial Part of the Hypothalamus

The medial part of the hypothalamus may be divided into three areas rostrocaudally and the most rostral area is further subdivided:

1. Supraoptic area:
   (a) Anterior hypothalamic group of nuclei;
   (b) Paraventricular nuclei } Preoptic nuclei in
   (c) Supraoptic nuclei   } lower vertebrates;
2. Middle or tuberal area;
3. Mamillary area.

The medial part of the hypothalamus receives afferent fibres from the hippocampus via the fornix, from the olfactory system via the stria terminalis and from the brain stem (ascending visceral afferents).

The efferent connections of the medial part of the hypothalamus can be divided into three groups, two of

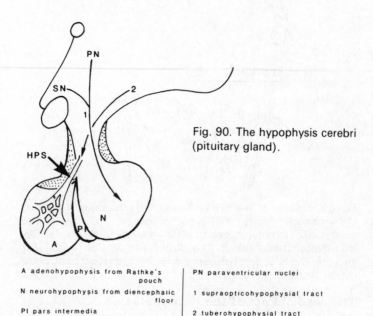

Fig. 90. The hypophysis cerebri (pituitary gland).

A adenohypophysis from Rathke's pouch	PN paraventricular nuclei
N neurohypophysis from diencephalic floor	1 supraopticohypophysial tract
PI pars intermedia	2 tuberohypophysial tract
pars tuberalis	HPS hypophysial portal system
SN supraoptic nuclei	

these groups being fibre connections and the third being vascular.

1. Fibre connections with other parts of the brain:
    (a) The mamillothalamic tract going to the anterior nucleus of the thalamus;
    (b) The mamillotegmental tract going to the midbrain tegmentum.
2. Fibre connections with the neurohypophysis (posterior lobe of the pituitary gland) (Fig. 90) which form two main tracts, the supraopticohypophysial tract going into the posterior lobe from the supraoptic and paraventricular nuclei and the tuberohypophysial tract going from the tuberal nuclei lying in the tuberal area into the neurohypophysis. Cells of the supraoptic and paraventricular nuclei are neurosecretory and transmit colloid droplets which pass along the axons of the cells producing them and are released at their endings in the neurohypophysis. The neurosecretory substance is assumed to be the precursors or the actual hormones of the neurohypophysis. The nuclei within the tuberal region also possess axons in which secretory granules can be demonstrated but these fibres of the tuberohypophysial tract are thought to contain 'releasing' hormones rather than hormones in their active form. These latter fibres end on capillary loops near the sinusoids of the hypophysial portal system (see later).
3. Vascular connections with the adenohypophysis (anterior lobe of the pituitary gland). The hypophysis receives two arteries from the internal carotid artery, the superior and inferior hypophysial arteries. The latter forms an arterial ring round the neurohypophysis and breaks up into sinusoids within its substance. The superior hypophysial artery supplies the upper part of the stalk of the pituitary gland and ends in intricate tufts of capillaries. These capillaries drain into descending vessels which break

up into vascular sinuses in the adenohypophysis and provide almost all the vascular supply to that structure. These vessels are referred to as the hypophysial portal system. The hypothalamus contains cells which produce pituitary releasing and inhibiting factors and these factors pass by axoplasmic flow within the axons of the cells releasing them to enter the capillaries and thus pass by the portal system to the adenohypophysis and so bring the synthesis and release of hormones by the adenohypophysis under hypothalamic control.

Functions of the Hypothalamus

The hypothalamus is related to all kinds of visceral activities. In essence, it exercises control over the internal milieu of the body. It is known that some hypothalamic regions give parasympathetic responses when stimulated and others give sympathetic responses. Clearly, the balance between these responses is necessary to maintain homeostasis. Regulation of body temperature, a very complex mechanism, is brought about by the anterior part of the hypothalamus which responds to high temperature and initiates the loss of heat and the posterior part of the hypothalamus which responds to low temperature and brings about mechanisms for the conservation of heat. These two antagonistic processes are continually inter-related and balanced against each other to meet the changing needs of the body so that a constant temperature is maintained.

The supraoptic and paraventricular nuclei are specifically concerned with water balance and they respond to the osmotic pressure of the blood. The tuberal region is known to be concerned with regulating food intake and in this region there is probably a satiety centre and a feeding centre. Pathological lesions in the hypothalamus can modify sexual development.

The importance of the hypothalamus is out of all proportion to its size. It is believed to be one of the major centres concerned with emotional expression because it integrates the parasympathetic and sympathetic components of the autonomic nervous system and it controls the pituitary gland by means of the portal system and by means of direct fibre tracts.

Suggested Items for Further Reading

M. L. BARR (1979). *The Human Nervous System*. Harper and Row.

M. B. CARPENTER (1978). *Core Text of Neuroanatomy*. Williams and Wilkins.

A. R. LURIA (1980). *Higher Cortical Functions in Man*. Basic Books, Inc.

Nature (1981). Volume **293** Number 5833, pp. 515–534. "The Neurosciences".

Scientific American (1979). Volume **241** Number 3. "The Brain".

INDEX